Third Edition

CHECKMATE
WORKBOOK

A WRITING REFERENCE
FOR CANADIANS

JOANNE BUCKLEY

TODD MERCER

PETER LAURIE

NELSON / EDUCATION

NELSON / EDUCATION

ISBN-13: 978-0-17-665669-0
ISBN-10: 0-17-665669-3

Cover Credit:

Greg Devitt Design

Contents

PREFACE

This Workbook is meant to accompany *Checkmate: A Canadian Writer's Reference, Third Edition*. It is set up to allow you, as a user of the handbook, to practise and reinforce your knowledge and skills on a variety of subjects related to the form and function of the English language.

The Workbook is divided into sections that match those in the handbook, notably Grammar, Common Sentence Errors, Punctuation, Sentence Structure and Style, Usage, Mechanics and Spelling, and topics related to ESL.

Each exercise comes complete with some answers or suggested answers and some items that have no answers provided that may be used as test material, if desired.

Instructors may find it useful to assign portions of these exercises to students whose work might benefit from additional practice in a particular area.

Students may use this workbook to improve their own skills, perhaps in response to grammatical or sentence structure problems pointed out by instructors in graded assignments. The Workbook is a useful tool to augment a writer's knowledge of a particular rules or set of rules in grammar, and it can help users of *Checkmate* identify and correct trouble spots in their own work.

As with *Checkmate*, much of the content of the exercises is Canadian. A variety of exercises have been provided to make the practice sessions entertaining and challenging for instructors, students, and other users of the handbook.

Chapter 9: GRAMMAR

1. Identify and Classify Nouns

If you have problems completing this exercise, review section 9-1A of *Checkmate: A Writing Reference for Canadians, Third Edition*.

The sentences below contain nouns of the following types:

1. Proper
2. Common
3. Concrete
4. Abstract
5. Collective
6. Non-count
7. Count
8. Possessive

Underline the nouns in each sentence and then identify what type of nouns they are. Some nouns may be classified in more than one way.

    EXAMPLE: The <u>book</u> opens with a <u>dedication</u> to <u>Naomi's father</u>.

                   3   4   8

1. Patrice will visit Calgary in December with her family.
2. The theme of the haiku poem was the essence of love.
3. Rain fell in Ucluelet, British Columbia for five long days.
4. The great writer, Vladimir Nabokov, held the butterfly in his outstretched hand.
5. Rocky's touchdown pass in the dying seconds of the game was a thing of beauty.
6. Sir John A. Macdonald led Canada to unity.
7. According to Richard J. Needham, people "won't steal anything that is red-hot or embedded in concrete."
8. The sun's rays warmed us and gentle breezes caressed the desert sands.
9. Hail wrought destruction on the crops in south central Saskatchewan.
10. Cities are good places in which to appreciate culture.

## 2.	Pronouns

If you have problems completing this exercise, review section 9-1C of *Checkmate: A Writing Reference for Canadians, Third Edition.*

Underline the correct pronoun within the parentheses. Then, underline any other pronouns in the sentence.

EXAMPLE: After David and Sylvie left, (<u>they</u>, them, their) phoned <u>us</u> on <u>their</u> cellphone to say how much <u>they</u> appreciated <u>our</u> hospitality.

1.	The Sindarthas are coming to our home at 4 p.m., and I expect (they, them, their) will stay for dinner.

2.	I hope you will join Dwayne and (I, me, he) for the evening news.

3.	When Gillian took (she, her, that) shopping, she parked her car by the police station and returned to find that it had been stolen.

4.	The money my rich uncle left to me is (me, my, mine) to do with as I wish; my brothers and sisters can spend (they, them, theirs) as they please.

5.	Drivers (which, who, that) travel in the passing lane should always keep to the posted speed limit.

6.	(This, These, That, Those) archer will probably make our next Olympic team if she continues her phenomenal progress.

7.	(Whose, who's, whom) minivan are we taking to my graduation?

8.	She carries (herself, himself, her) very well and plans to be the world's next wealthy supermodel.

9.	Since Marion and I live only a block apart, we frequently visit (ourselves, each other, one another).

10.	(Everyone, Each, Anybody) wanted to come to my 1980s nostalgia party.

Chapter 9: *Grammar*

3.   Verbs

If you have problems completing this exercise, review section 9-1D of *Checkmate: A Writing Reference for Canadians, Third Edition*.

Underline the verbs. Make sure that you underline main verbs, helping (auxiliary) verbs, and modals.

EXAMPLE: The infielder <u>had caught</u> the fly ball.

1.   The starter fired the gun.

2.   Tornadoes occasionally occur in south central Ontario.

3.   My father has been a widower for six years.

4.   Margaret detests elevators.

5.   The wet dog shook.

6.   I feel anxious about the final chemistry examination.

7.   She had wanted to be a lumberjack since her early childhood.

8.   You should have written to me before arriving at my doorstep for a six-week holiday.

9.   They take singing lessons with my brother-in-law.

10. We will be visiting all the castles in an eastern region of Portugal during our trip.

11. Colm had painted the ceiling with an oil-based paint.

12. He approached every essay assignment with an open mind.

13. Don't give me any back talk!

14. If I were wealthier, I would travel more.

15. The convicted prisoner was taken to the execution room.

4.   Adjectives, Articles, and Adverbs

If you have problems completing this exercise, review section 9-1E of *Checkmate: A Writing Reference for Canadians, Third Edition.*

Underline adjectives once. Consider the articles *a*, *an*, and *the* as limiting adjectives. Under each article, indicate whether it is a definite article (with the letter *D*) or an indefinite article (with the letter *I*.) Underline adverbs twice.

EXAMPLE: After a full night of partying, Jason is sleeping soundly in the lounge.

I   D

1. The old mattress is very comfortable.

2. Her novel echoes a story from classical literature.

3. Ali enthusiastically approached the learning task with childlike curiosity.

4. It is wishful thinking to completely base your retirement plans on the hope that you will win a provincial lottery.

5. A victimless crime is still an unacceptable act.

6. The elderly master of ceremonies read the winners' names slowly but clearly.

7. Climate change is an extremely important environmental problem.

8. Giovanni plays the classical guitar really well.

9. Fortunately, when the accident-prone stuntman fell out of the helicopter, there was a soft haystack below him.

10. The Korean exchange student can run faster than anyone I know, but she is certainly not the fastest sprinter on campus.

5.   Prepositions, Conjunctions, and Interjections

If you have problems completing this exercise, review sections 9-1G to 9-1I of *Checkmate: A Writing Reference for Canadians, Third Edition.*

In each sentence, underline prepositions once, underline conjunctions twice, and highlight interjections in yellow.

EXAMPLE: <u>*Oh*</u>, take your dog <u>to</u> the opera if you must, <u><u>but</u></u> don't sit <u>near</u> me.

1. Allanna is not associated with the group that wrote graffiti on washroom walls or the mob that overturned the statue of the university president.

2. Yes, I will return the book to the library and pay the accumulated fine.

3. You can slip the completed essay under the professor's office door or ask a secretary to place it in the mail box.

4. Melody's room is opposite mine in the residence, yet she studies so hard that I have not seen her in ages.

5. I am not registering for the intramural hockey league this year, so there is no point buying new equipment.

6. Neither sleet nor snow will keep mail carriers or plumbers from finding their way to our door.

7. No, you cannot drive a motorcycle without a helmet and a valid driver's license.

8. It is wise to live within your means; however, you have to spend money to make money.

9. Not only Carol Shields but also Rohinton Mistry was nominated for the prestigious literary award.

10. Ouch, it hurt when I was struck by lightning on the shoulder and under the arm.

6.   Sentence Subjects

If you have problems completing this exercise, review section 9-2A of *Checkmate: A Writing Reference for Canadians, Third Edition*.

Underline the complete subject once. Underline the simple subject twice. If the subject is not provided but is understood, write it in and place square brackets around it.

EXAMPLE: <u>A sudden <u>flash</u> of lightning</u> terrified the dogs.

1. The challenging and breathtaking highway snakes through the Alberni Valley to Tofino.

2. The mild climate of Victoria, British Columbia attracts many university students and retirees.

3. Margaret Atwood and Mordecai Richler are famous Canadian novelists.

4. Red and black poppies appear on lapels across the nation during November.

5. For a time, Vancouver, British Columbia, and Lucerne, Switzerland, were in contention for the Winter Olympics.

6. Act now or not at all.

7. There is a distinct possibility that a special guest will attend the convocation ceremony.

8. There were two security guards in the large crowd.

9. Does Gillian think she will get away with the deception?

10. After considerable debate, the championship game will be on Friday.

Chapter 9: *Grammar*

7. Sentence Objects and Complements

If you have problems completing this exercise, review section 9-2B of *Checkmate: A Writing Reference for Canadians, Third Edition*.

Place square brackets around any subject, verb, subject complement, direct object, indirect object, or object. Then, identify the sentence part using the abbreviations below.

S = Subject   DO = Direct Object

V = Verb   IO = Indirect Object

SC = Subject Complement   OC = Object Complement

    EXAMPLE: [Who] [gave] [me] [this box of Band-Aids] [as a birthday gift]?

                S   V   IO   DO   OC

1. Adolescence is not a bed of roses.

2. The foul ball hit the first base umpire.

3. The young author published a second collection of poems.

4. A second collection of poems was published by the young author.

5. Who sold you that incredible new Bruce Springsteen CD?

6. The student called his drama instructor a fruit cake.

7. The basketball team wins.

8. You give me a five-dollar bill, and I will give you five loonies.

9. The captain of the debating team was a senior.

10. Several souvenirs were bought by our friends.

8. Prepositional Phrases

If you have problems completing this exercise, review section 9-3A of *Checkmate: A Writing Reference for Canadians, Third Edition*.

Underline the prepositional phrase or phrases in each sentence. Below the phrase, indicate whether it is an adverb or an adjective. Draw an arrow to connect the prepositional phrase to the noun or verb it modifies.

EXAMPLE: He placed the book <u>on the shelf</u> and opened the top drawer <u>of his desk.</u>

   adverb   adjective

1. The film on Canada's contribution to World War I is very graphic.

2. The Pattersons ate dinner before driving to the cottage.

3. The hockey team travelled to Lethbridge.

4. The show dogs in the judging ring are absolutely stunning.

5. Fydor Dostoevsky wrote *Crime and Punishment* in 1866.

6. Dale purchased a new car with bucket seats.

7. The squirrel scurries across the top of our backyard fence.

8. You can identify a cardinal by its unique colouring.

9. The Museum of Civilization in Ottawa was designed by Douglas Cardinal.

10. The professors met in private to discuss the English courses for next year.

9. Verbal Phrases

If you have problems completing this exercise, review section 9-3B of *Checkmate: A Writing Reference for Canadians, Third Edition*.

Underline the verbal phrase or phrases in each sentence. On the line below the sentence, identify what type of verbal phrase it is and its function.

   EXAMPLE: The last entrant refused <u>to quit.</u>

   Infinitive phrase; it is the direct object of the verb *refused*.

1. The rabbit, bounding and dodging, crossed Lucy's path.

   _____

2. Standing is not good for your circulation.

   _____

3. Being fifty years of age, Jeb's father gets a cheaper car insurance rate.

   _____

4. The purpose of any enthusiastic marathoner is to win.

   _____

5. To reach the summit was the climbers' ultimate goal.

   _____

6. Neutered and regularly vaccinated, a male dog has a better chance of reaching old age.

   _____

7. Thankfully, the pedestrians avoided the badly shattered glass.

   _____

8. Any interested and qualified students should apply within.

   _____

9. It is always better to give than to receive.

   _____

10. Andrew decided to go home for the spring break.

   _____

10.   Subordinate Clauses

If you have problems completing this exercise, review section 9-3E of *Checkmate: A Writing Reference for Canadians, Third Edition*.

Underline the subordinate clause in each sentence. Underneath the subordinate clause, indicate whether it functions as a noun, adjective, or adverb.

EXAMPLE: <u>When the clock struck 3 p.m</u>., everyone headed for the cafeteria.

adverb

1. Switzerland is one of the few countries in the world where the trains arrive and depart on time.

2. Address the letter to whom you wish.

3. Promptly complete the homework that is assigned to you.

4. I had a relaxing weekend because I had completed my final examinations.

5. Raginder will proof my term biology essay when he is good and ready.

6. We think that Patrick Dorn is the best candidate as our student representative.

7. Whichever career path she chooses will be the correct one.

8. The movie that I saw on the weekend featured Adam Sandler in a very unconventional role.

9. My mark was better than the grade I received in the first term.

10. The visiting professor, who has won a Nobel Prize in chemistry, gave a scintillating lecture on science and ethics.

11. After taking a cruise down the Danube, they ate goulash in one of Budapest's best open-air restaurants.

12. What you learned on the CRC station about the political race is probably biased.

11.   Sentence Types

If you have problems completing this exercise, review section 9-4 of *Checkmate: A Writing Reference for Canadians, Third Edition*.

Under each sentence, indicate the sentence structure (simple, compound, complex, or compound/complex). Then, indicate the function of the sentence (declarative, imperative, interrogative, or exclamatory).

EXAMPLE: Do you vow to love, honour, and obey your wife?

<u>simple; interrogative</u>

1. Coincidentally, the convicts were wanted in British Columbia and in Nova Scotia, too.

   _____

2. Are you planning to stay in the residence during reading break?

   _____

3. Several critics think *The Sun Also Rises* is Hemingway's best novel; a small minority of critics do not consider it to be a major work.

   _____

4. You must do it now!

   _____

5. The person who helped me carry the package to my car became my wife within a year.

   _____

6. Once Cronenberg achieved popular success, the Canadian director confounded his audience, and he began making more artistic films.

   _____

7. As a newspaper reporter, Ernest Hemingway once wrote for *The Toronto Star*.

_____

8. Dame Cicely was among the most renowned stage actors of her generation, yet she had no formal theatrical training.

_____

9. The Pawalskis had venison steaks that Earl had stored in the freezer.

_____

10. While I watched dumbfounded, Gillian entered the room and sat down, crushing the divan.

_____

11. Drop your weapons, and come out with your hands up.

_____

12. The Andersons ate moose hamburgers, and the Pawalskis consumed venison steaks that Earl had kept stored in the freezer.

_____

Chapter 10: COMMON SENTENCE ERRORS

1.   Correcting Sentence Fragments

If you have problems completing this exercise, review section 10-1 of *Checkmate: A Writing Reference for Canadians, Third Edition*. Selected answers appear at the back of this workbook.

Decide whether each group of words is a complete sentence or not. If even one of the word groups is a fragment, make it a complete sentence by adding the missing sentence element or elements. You may want to combine a fragment with an accompanying complete sentence or another fragment to create one complete sentence. If the word group is a complete sentence, indicate this in the space provided. Finally, in brackets, briefly explain any sentence-fragment problems.

EXAMPLE: In the heat of the night.

REVISED: In the heat of the night, I turn up the air conditioner. (phrase with no subject or verb)

1. Dove for the ball.

    _____

2. After I cook my famous rib recipe.

    _____

3.   It's all in the sauce.

    _____

4. Had come to Spuzzum Community College. Before I enrolled.

    _____

5. Jason stayed up all night to finish his term paper. After he checked for e-mail messages.

    _____

6. While I stood on a jagged rock watching the glorious Tofino sunset and munched sunflower seeds.

_____

7. I became a contestant on the television show *Fear Factor*. With an unsettled stomach.

_____

8. In my darkest moments.

_____

9. Tammy wanted to see both Academy Award–nominated movies. But only had the time and money to view one.

_____

10. Any discussion of diseases requiring more research funding must include the major ones that kill Canadians. For example heart disease, cancer, and diabetes.

_____

2.   Editing to Correct Sentence Fragments

If you have problems completing this exercise, review sections 10-1 A-D of *Checkmate: A Writing Reference for Canadians, Third Edition.*

Rewrite the passage below to correct any problems with sentence fragments.

Family reunions! Definitely are not my idea of a good time. Judging parents, rude or inebriated uncles, ultra-nosy aunts (or ones who talk to me like I'm still three years old), and rug-rat nieces and nephews. Eating fifteen different varieties of potato salad. Because most of my relatives are too cheap to buy a substantial meat dish. Wouldn't it be great if everyone chipped in about thirty dollars? For a buffet restaurant. Then at least we would be sure to get a balanced meal. Not to mention a little variety among Canada's major food groups.

Another family-reunion pet peeve. Conversation. Or lack thereof. As a college student. I'm forced to attend these dreaded affairs. At the peril of having my income flow stopped immediately. After I get there. It seems that all assembled relatives grill me on the standard topics. For example, my academic performance, my love life, career prospects, salary expectation in my field. And, of course, the reason for pursuing any line of work from the perspective of the chronically middle aged. Sick leave. Disability benefits. And who can forget? Pensions.

After checking my watch every thirty seconds. Finally. Time to go. But wait! I have to say goodbye to every relative in attendance. Which takes at least another half hour. If I don't, I'll be officially excommunicated from my extended family. For the cardinal sin. Thoughtlessness. By the time I get to my car. I'm thinking the once-in-a-lifetime party that every girl. Who I've ever wanted to date will be at is now over. Oh well. At least I saw ninety-six-year-old Aunt Agatha. Thank goodness. Family reunions. Only happen once every six months.

3.   Avoiding Comma Splices and Fused Sentences

If you have problems completing this exercise, review section 10-2 of *Checkmate: A Writing Reference for Canadians, Third Edition*. Selected answers appear at the back of this workbook.

Correct each comma splice or fused sentence by applying strategies presented in *Checkmate*. Use the space provided if significant rewriting is required.

EXAMPLE: The company president is incredibly busy she still grows her own vegetables.

REVISED: Although the company president is incredibly busy, she still grows her own vegetables.

1. Cape Bonavista is located on Newfoundland's northeast coast it is considered a possible site where John Cabot first landed in the New World in 1497.

_____

_____

2. The late Arthur Erickson, one of Canada's most renowned architects, was instrumental in the design of Simon Fraser University, however, he also gained international attention as the architect for the Canadian Embassy in Washington.

_____

_____

3. Paul Henderson scored probably the most dramatic goal in Canadian hockey history, it won the 1972 Canada–Soviet Hockey Series.

_____

_____

4. In the reproductive process of conifers, one male gamete fertilizes the egg the other degenerates.

_____

_____

5. Sir Wilfrid Laurier desired to correct abuses arising from fundamental changes in society, he focused his attention on two bills, which ultimately resulted in his defeat.

_____

_____

6. Oscar Peterson's first music instructor, his sister Daisy, went on to become a respected piano teacher in the Montreal black community, her later pupils included the fine jazz musicians Oliver Jones, Joe Sealy, and Reg Wilson.

_____

_____

4.   Review: Sentence Fragments, Comma Splices, and Fused Sentences

If you have problems completing this exercise, review sections 10-1 and 10-2 of *Checkmate: A Writing Reference for Canadians, Third Edition*.

Edit the personal essay to correct any problems with sentence fragments, comma splices, and fused sentences.

The fax machine was supposedly invented to help humankind, however, now it has become an instrument of marketing terrorism.

I am the victim of innumerable junk fax transmissions, I have the greatest empathy for anyone who has been stalked by the sleeper cells of junk fax terrorists. My personal harassment started shortly after I purchased a fax machine, I made the technological leap to a dedicated fax line.

Soon, my basement office was the receiving centre for a vast home-shopping network. All manner of commercial missives spewed off my fax rollers, much to my amazement, I learned that I could buy oak flooring, get a cellphone for $0, subscribe to Internet magazines, and receive cash for my empty laser printer cartridges or old telephone system. I could also advertise my logo and a commercial message on "custom imprinted ceramic coffee mugs," pave my driveway at pre-season rates, buy discount vacations to Aruba, entertain clients at a billiards lounge/bistro, buy term insurance or mutual funds, and install a water cooler, and if I needed cash to finance these "must-have" products and services, I could plug into a line of credit at "rock-bottom" interest rates with no questions asked.

Like many modern households, mine has a number of telephone lines. One for business, one for personal calls, one for the fax machine, and one for the Internet. Invariably, I was in the middle of an important work project or just about to sit down to dinner, one line's phone would ring and I'd pick up the receiver only to hear an annoying fax tone. The process continued every two minutes for each phone line in the house. Ironically, the junk faxes' advertisers boasted that they could increase my productivity by 50%, they were decreasing it by 75% because I was constantly playing "musical phones," having to get up to answer junk fax calls.

Some faxes came from anonymous marketers, others provided phone numbers I could call to have my name removed from the master marketing list, but this struck me as highly unfair since the onus was on me to correct the problem.

What puzzled me most was how the fax marketers got my number in the first place. My research led to a telephone company vice president. Who explained there were companies whose sole purpose is to create fax number lists. They obtain list entries by calling any random sequences of phone numbers. They hit your number and get a fax tone. Congratulations. You make the list. These companies then sell the list to telemarketing companies. I was told I could phone the number on the bottom of a junk fax to have my name removed from their list. This proved small consolation because the list compilers could have sold my phone numbers to other telemarketing firms.

Junk faxes are like a virus that's out of control, the virus is living off my time and fax paper!

5.   Agreement of Subject and Verb, No. 1

If you have problems completing this exercise, review all of section 10-3 in *Checkmate: A Writing Reference for Canadians, Third Edition*. Selected answers appear at the back of this workbook.

In each sentence below, first underline the subject; then, if necessary, correct the verb so that it agrees with the subject. If the sentence has no subject–verb problem, write "correct" beside it.

EXAMPLE: The last three weeks of summer school is always the worst.

REVISED: The last three <u>weeks </u>of summer school **are** always the worst.

1. My mathematics teacher live near the university grounds.

2. In my opinion, the final two chapters of the book is the most thrilling.

3. The students on the fifth floor win the prize for the most outlandish costumes.

4. The Oscar-winning actor, along with her co-stars, were at a gala party after the ceremony.

5. Laurel and Hardy stars in *Babes in Toyland* and *A Chump at Oxford*.

6. Bacon and eggs were the only thing the Levers would eat for breakfast on a Sunday morning.

7. Every man, woman, and child have the right to freedom from persecution.

8. Neither the prime minister nor his top advisor know how to resolve the economic crisis.

9. Somebody have to stand up and make his or her voice heard above the crowd, but nobody do.

10. Everyone realizes that he committed the crime; however, without sufficient evidence, nothing can be done.

11. None of the crops are ready to be harvested.

12. Only some of the money from the bank robbery have been recovered.

6.   Agreement of Subject and Verb, No. 2

If you have problems completing this exercise, review all of section 10-3 in *Checkmate: A Writing Reference for Canadians, Third Edition*. Selected answers appear at the back of this workbook.

First, highlight the subject in each sentence; then, in the space provided, write the verb that agrees with the subject.

1. The jury ____ until a verdict is reached.

    (deliberates, deliberate)

2. The jury ____ their separate decisions to a member who acts as the foreperson.

    (gives, give)

3. One-quarter of the public works budget ____ allocated for snow removal.

    (has been, have been)

4. About three-quarters of the shareholders ____ at the annual meeting.

    (was, were)

5. There ____ three important reasons why I support Marika's proposal.

    (is, are)

6. Hiding in the corner ____ the two cowering, terrified, pathetic thieves.

    (was, were)

7. Our dogs, Lucy and Ace, ____ like kids to us.

    (is, are)

8. His thinking ____ that the land values will go up after the factory opens.

    (is, are)

9. The judges who ____ the final decision ____ not like Great Danes.

    (makes, make)   (does, do)

10. One of the issues we have to consider ____ how the development plan will affect wildlife.

    (is, are)

11. Only one of the flight attendants ____ to be on duty.

    (appears, appear)

12. The news ____ not been good concerning her chances for a full recovery.

    (have, has)

Chapter 10: *Common Sentence Errors*

7. Editing for Subject–Verb Agreement

If you have problems completing this exercise, review all of section 10-3 in *Checkmate: A Writing Reference for Canadians, Third Edition*. Selected answers appear at the back of this workbook.

Identify the subject in each sentence. Then, underline the verb within the brackets that agrees with the subject.

Capitalizing on a Hot Market

Shelly Burns (is/are) one hot commodity.

In her final year of a three-year Fire Protection Technology Program at Grosvenor College, Burns (has/have) 17 job interviews awaiting her over a two-week period in early March. And before her late-April graduation, Burns, 24, (expects/expect) to have at least four or five serious job offers to mull over, many with large and prestigious American companies.

Burns' situation (is/are) not unique. There (is/are) a high demand for Grosvenor graduates dictated by the scorching hot job market. Grosvenor's Fire Protection Program (has/have) been around since 1972 and (is/are) the largest of its kind at the college level in North America.

While "fire protection" may conjure up images of hearty men and women in sou'westers hauling hoses up a ladder, students taking the program (emerges/emerge) prepared for a variety of careers.

At the end of the first year of study, students (chooses/choose) between a two-year program, which covers sprinkler installation and service, and a three-year technologist program, which concentrates on alarm and sprinkler system design.

Recently, the job market (seems/seem) particularly hot in sprinkler design. The programs (has/have) had almost 100 percent placement over the past three years. Most employer interest (comes/come) from the United States, where about 70 percent of Grosvenor graduates (accepts/accept) positions.

A major reason for the Fire Protection Program's success (is/are) that it responds to industry needs. Some employers (wants/want) to see students with more on-the-job experience. As a result, the program (is/are) introducing a paid co-op program for this upcoming semester.

As Shelly Burns (attests/attest), one of the most employment-directed programs at the college (is/are) Fire Protection Technology. Anyone who (completes/complete) the program will surely agree.

8.   Irregular Verbs

If you have problems completing this exercise, review sections 10-4A and B of *Checkmate: A Writing Reference for Canadians, Third Edition*. Selected answers appear at the back of this workbook.

Fill in each blank with the correct form of the irregular verb in parentheses.

EXAMPLE: (bear) Micky <u>bore</u> most of the weight when they carried the hide-a-bed up the stairs.

1. (sing) Last night my brother-in-law ___ the role of the barber in *The Barber of Seville*, a role he has ___ many times in the past.

2. (freeze) When the hunter saw the grizzly bear, he ___ in his tracks.

3. (hang) Lucille ___ the family portrait prominently in the den.

4. (hang) The convicted killer was ___ by the neck until he was dead.

5. (bite, seek) After he was ___ by the salivating dog, Jerome ___ medical attention at the nearest hospital.

6. (dream, slay) I ___ that the menacing dragon was ___ by the valiant knight.

7. (hide, prove) The bank robbers ___ the money where it ___ impossible to find.

8. (rise) Ted had not ___ so early in the morning for years.

9. (drink, leave) The punch was ___ before the last of the wedding guests had ___.

10. (dive, forbid) The teenagers ___ into the lake from the old train bridge even though they had been ___ to do so on many occasions.

11. (lay) Jennifer ___ the reference books on the top shelf last Wednesday.

12. (lie) The kidnappers had ___ in wait for about an hour before their victims finally arrived.

13. (lay) He had ___ the dozen red roses on the dining room table so that his fiancée would notice them.

14. (lie) My Uncle Leo ___ down for seven hours after he ate twelve helpings of Thanksgiving dinner.

15. (sit) The nude model had ___ motionless for what seemed like hours while the art students sketched her.

9.   Verbs with *-s* and *-ed* Endings and Verbs Not to Omit

If you have problems completing this exercise, review sections 10-4 C, D, and E of *Checkmate: A Writing Reference for Canadians, Third Edition*. Selected answers appear at the back of this workbook.

Edit each sentence to correct any problems with verbs. Rewrite question 12 so that all verb endings are correct and all verbs or verb phrases are complete.

EXAMPLE: Jeb always proofread his essays carefully and don't ever recall having a mistake on a paper he submit for marking.

REVISED: Jeb always **proofreads** his essays carefully and **doesn't** ever recall having a mistake on a paper he **submitted** for marking.

1. I keeps my ski poles in the closet so I can easily find them.
2. Editing require a good eye, a sharp pencil, and a complete library of up-to-date reference books.
3. I takes half an hour to climb the long and winding hill on my bicycle, but the Canadian Olympic Cycling team take only five minutes to reach the top.
4. The theatre manager have not had a night with such low attendance before, and he don't think it will happen again.
5. Last May, the controversial bill was pass after considerable debate in the provincial legislature.
6. In her native Guatemala, Ms. Rodriguez practise medicine for over fifteen years.
7. For years the labour leader had champion the cause of workplace safety.
8. My overdue rent cheque was deposit in the property manager's night mailbox.
9. Yesterday, the coach escort the hobble athlete to the dressing room for treatment on her hamstring.
10. After opening the box containing the swing set, Jessica's parents found the instructions missing.
11. Consumer confidence declined since the corporate scandals first struck.
12. The average hockey fan in Canada suffer a lot. He/she don't have much recourse when the local team do badly. In fact, a typical Canadian hockey fan probably learn to deal with ongoing frustration years ago. He/she have watched the local team fall to playoff defeat time and again. Dutifully, when a spate of injuries strike during the regular season, he/she watch the wound home team hobble along. The typical Canuck fan have no doubt develop countless strategies for coping with failure. To make matters worse, as player salaries has gone up, Canadian fan expectations gone down.

Chapter 10: *Common Sentence Errors*   23

10.   Verb Tenses

If you have problems completing this exercise, review section 10-4F of *Checkmate: A Writing Reference for Canadians, Third Edition*. Selected answers appear at the back of this workbook.

Correct any verb tense errors in the sentences below.

EXAMPLE: By the time the guests arrived, we consumed all the beverages.

REVISED: By the time the guests arrived, we **had** consumed all the beverages.

1. At the end of James Joyce's short story "The Dead," the main character, Gabriel, achieved an epiphany.

2. Sir Isaac Newton was instrumental in helping us understand that gravity has caused things to have weight and fall to the ground when they are dropped.

3. Sir Francis Bacon (1561–1626) has been saying, "A prudent question is one-half of wisdom."

4. Many of the communities were not built when the power dam was constructed.

5. While the Smiths searched for the missing girl along the beach, we had searched behind the cabin.

6. Bernice wanted to pass the written examination next month.

7. Having risked his own life, he saved the drowning child.

8. Studying conscientiously for weeks, Elsa passed the final examination with ease.

9. You will be late if you will take the detour through Markham.

10. The rye bread has become moldy since I have taken it out of the package.

11. We had already eaten dinner when they have arrived.

12. The actor has trained in London, England before coming to Niagara-on-the-Lake.

11. Using the Subjunctive Mood Appropriately

If you have problems completing this exercise, review section 10-4G of *Checkmate: A Writing Reference for Canadians, Third Edition*. Selected answers appear at the back of this workbook.

Correct any problems with the mood of verbs in the sentences below. If the sentence has no errors, write "correct" beside it.

EXAMPLE: Every day, I wish it was snowboarding season.

REVISED: Every day, I wish it **were** snowboarding season.

1. It is critical that the emergency-room physician is briefed on an incoming patient's condition.

2. They insisted that the lawyer prints copies of the uncle's will in triplicate.

3. My neighbour wishes that she was the winner of the provincial lottery so that she can buy new windows.

4. If Denis was the only man on earth, Stella would still not go out with him.

5. She could run for the office of president of the United States if she was not born in British Columbia.

6. If the meeting finishes on time, he will be home before 6 p.m.

7. We wish that our father was closer to Ontario so he could visit more often.

8. The coroner's report recommends that a retaining wall is erected around the hairpin turn.

9. The doctor urges that Jason loses weight to help lower his cholesterol.

10. If this were a sunny day, I would paint the house, cut the lawn, and take the dogs for a walk.

11. Suffice it to say, they agree.

12. It is required that the seller presents himself or herself at the municipal office at 1 p.m.

13. I'd invest in real estate if I was a wealthy woman.

14. If he arrive late, I will give him a lecture on punctuality.

15. Despite our long personal history together, she greeted me as though I was a stranger.

12.   Active versus Passive Voice

If you have problems completing this exercise, review section 10-4H of *Checkmate: A Writing Reference for Canadians, Third Edition*. Selected answers appear at the back of this workbook.

Part 1: Rewrite each sentence in the active voice.

a. After a lengthy and dangerous chase, the escaped criminals were caught by the RCMP in Lethbridge.

_____

b. Each week, the domestic exploits of the Osbourne family were watched by millions of North American viewers.

_____

c. A lawsuit was filed by the owner of the red sports car against the driver of the cream-coloured minivan who broadsided him.

_____

d. In certain parts of the world, eating chocolate-covered insects is considered a gourmet experience.

_____

e. Edward was given an entry-level management position by a new Canadian telecommunications company.

_____

Part 2: Rewrite each sentence in the passive voice.

a. The disease divides into three main groups.

_____

b. Trees and plants take in water through their roots and gradually release that water into the air

through their leaves.

_____

c. Heavy snowfalls closed the school.

_____

d. Scientists designed the new plasma television to increase your viewing pleasure.

_____

e. During World War II, government officials interned Canadians of Japanese descent in camps

within the Kootenay region of British Columbia.

_____

13. Pronoun–Antecedent Agreement

If you have problems completing this exercise, review section 10-5A of *Checkmate: A Writing Reference for Canadians, Third Edition*. Selected answers appear at the back of this workbook.

Part 1: Underline the pronoun that provides pronoun–antecedent agreement.

a. Everyone should do (his, her, his or her, their) part to reduce air pollution caused by automobile exhaust emissions.

b. If anyone wants to buy a ticket for the annual ski trip, (he, she, he or she, they) will have to do it by this coming Thursday.

c. Each dentist must ensure (he, she, he or she, they) carries adequate malpractice insurance.

d. The crowd stood up and cheered as (he, she, he or she, they, it) acknowledged the centre fielder's game-winning home run.

e. After the game, the capacity crowd slowly made (his, her, their, its) way to the various exits around the Rogers Centre.

f. The coach and the players were extremely tired after (his and their, its, their) long bus trip back from the game in Sault Ste. Marie.

g. Neither the team's general manager nor the players were prepared to share (his, their and his, their) feelings about the looming threat of a strike.

h. The faculty held (his and hers, their, its) Christmas party at a local country club.

Part 2: Rewrite the sentences using more than one strategy to correct pronoun–antecedent agreement problems. Use three strategies in (a) and two strategies in (b).

a. Each student learns the curriculum at their own pace.

_____

_____

_____

b. Either Ellie or Nathan will have his essay selected as the best undergraduate essay for the

previous year.

_____

_____

14. Making Pronoun References Clear

If you have problems completing this exercise, review section 10-5B of *Checkmate: A Writing Reference for Canadians, Third Edition*.

Rewrite each sentence to correct problems with clarity of pronoun references. In some cases, there are a number of acceptable alternatives. You may need to add ideas or words to make sentences clear.

EXAMPLE: When Susan visited Sally, she did not know that she would soon catch pneumonia.

REVISED: When Susan visited Sally, she did not know that **Sally** would soon catch pneumonia.

1. Stella informed her mother that the telephone call was for her.

_____

2. In Martin Amis' *Heavy Water*, he ponders what it would be like if poets were highly paid and Hollywood screenwriters were not.

_____

_____

3. Hugh followed the steps in the chemistry experiments religiously, but they didn't produce the reactions shown in the textbook.

_____

_____

4. Marci drove her Toyota into a power pole, severely damaging it.

_____

_____

5. In the article "A New Perspective on Biology," it says that new research into the biological aspects of human personality is changing assumptions.

    _____

    _____

6. The movie holds its suspense right to the end. For example, in the final scene, they never allow the viewer to see who fired the gun.

    _____

    _____

7. In bygone days, you could purchase a steak dinner for a dollar.

    _____

8. Archaeologists discovered a tool on the shore that was thousands of years old.

    _____

15.   Using Pronoun Case Correctly

If you have problems completing this exercise, review section 10-5C of *Checkmate: A Writing Reference for Canadians, Third Edition*.

Underline the correct pronoun case(s) in each sentence.

1. Miquel asked Rachel and (I, me) to accompany (he, him) and his wife to the concert.

2. Between you and (I, me), (I, me) think an outsider stole the money from the dorm piggy bank.

3. The driving instructor asked (he, him) to do a parallel park during the examination.

4. After much deliberation, the judges of the literary competition awarded the coveted literary prize to (he and I, him and me).

5. Despite our many differences, Chuck and (I, me) have resolved to behave in a civil manner while in public.

6. I'm not sure whether Don or (I, me, myself) will take the call from (he, him).

7. The lawyer forwarded a copy of the contract to Margaret and (I, me, myself).

8. The executive members of the marketing team—Davin, Aurturo, and (I, me)—gave the presentation to representatives of the client—Mr. Phillips, Ms. Edwards, and (she, her).

9. Let's you and (I, me) call the whole thing off.

10. (We, us) University of Victoria alumni are spread out all over Canada, but it is a little harder to find (we, us) Rhodes scholars.

11. Last semester, Cedric studied day and night, and (he, him) received much higher marks than (I, me).

12. Although our neighbours were a little shocked to see a college student out trick-or-treating, they gave the same number of treats to my four-year-old niece and (I, me).

13. After they became engaged, my sister and her fiancé asked (I, me) to give the toast to the bride.

14. The people in Oakville overwhelmingly voted to send (she, her) to represent (they, them) in Ottawa.

15. The don at the university residence strongly objected to (he, him, his) keeping a full-grown Bengal tiger in his room.

16.   Correctly Using *Who* and *Whom*

If you have problems completing this exercise, review section 10-5D of *Checkmate: A Writing Reference for Canadians, Third Edition.*

Underline *who, whom, whoever,* or *whomever* to indicate the correct pronoun case.

1. (Who/Whom) did the students choose to represent them at the environmental conference?

2. (Whoever, Whomever) attends the conference will need to make a serious commitment of his or her time, money, and energy.

3. At the conference, a scholarship prize is awarded to (whoever, whomever) makes the most compelling and convincing speech on a current environmental issue.

4. At present, organizers do not know (who, whom) will be the keynote speaker this year.

5. There are several excellent candidates, and you can be sure that (whoever, whomever) the selection committee chooses will make an outstanding presentation.

6. Possible speakers can be narrowed down somewhat, since the committee plans to contact only people (who, whom) are sympathetic to conference organizers' political agenda.

7. My stepmother, (who, whom) is no longer alive, loved to travel to Portugal.

8. The relative to (who, whom) I owe my great sense of humour is my maternal grandmother.

9. (Who, whom) should I ask for information about pursuing a career in veterinary medicine?

10. Do you know Marika, (who, whom) is the biology teaching assistant?

11. It was definitely she (who, whom) I saw at the reference library.

12. Happiness is there for (whoever, whomever) is willing to schedule time for it.

17.   Pronoun Review

If you have problems completing this exercise, review all of section 10-5 in *Checkmate: A Writing Reference for Canadians, Third Edition.*

Edit the passage to correct any pronoun problems.

    EXAMPLE: I remember my first kayak rescue class as if they were yesterday.

    REVISED: I remember my first kayak rescue class as if **it** were yesterday.

I remember my first kayak rescue class as if they were yesterday. There were about eight of we, and us met at the university pool. First, everyone had to launch their small plastic kayak. Then, we all met at the centre of the pool, where our instructor, Dougal, coached we in some safety procedures. One technique was called the Eskimo Bow Rescue. Me watched in horror as he demonstrated them with three other students. First, Barbara, the person role-playing the capsized person, had to stay in his kayak, then roll over and remain seated in the inverted boat, all the time completely submerged. While in this position, her reached her hands to the surface and thumped on the overturned hull to attract the attention of their rescuers. In this simulation, they were Theresa and William, which were supposed to be travelling with she. Once them noticed Barbara's banging, their were to meet around the capsized kayak to rescue him. As she blindly swept her arms back and forth, if everything went according to plan, her groping hands would somehow find a friendly bow, and use one of it to hoist she and her kayak out of the water with a flick of her hips.

    This seemed horrifyingly dangerous to I. The weakness of the plan, who might work fine in a swimming pool where people were expecting something to happen, was that on the rolling open ocean, they would probably take a good deal more than thirty seconds for rescuers to notice you and then manoeuvre their boats into a rescue position. I doubt that anyone which has accidentally capsized at sea would patiently hang around upside down hoping that others would get to them before they ran out of air.

18. Using Adverbs and Adjectives Correctly

If you have problems completing this exercise, review section 10-6 of *Checkmate: A Writing Reference for Canadians, Third Edition.*

Edit the sentences to correct errors in the use of adverbs or adjectives.

> EXAMPLE: The physician said it was the worse case of whooping cough she had ever seen.

> REVISED: The physician said it was the **worst** case of whooping cough she had ever seen.

1. The Formula 1 racing car driven by Paul Tracy sped quickly and powerful around the track.

2. There are always employment opportunities for journalism graduates who can write good.

3. Skeptics were not real optimistic about the prospects for success of the young starlet's second marriage within a year.

4. Gavin watched the relentlessly horizon.

5. My dry-cleaned cashmere sweater felt very softly, and when I put it on, the garment smelled freshly.

6. He felt bad because his behaviour at Myra's party had so been so atrociously bad.

7. Of the six candidates we interviewed for the vacant human resources officer position, Eloise was by far the better applicant.

8. Mother Teresa was probably one of the lesser selfish people I studied in the entire history course.

9. All things considered, between the Dream and Shaq, I think Shaq was the best NBA centre.

10. We concluded that Pele was a most dominating athlete than Michael Jordan and that the great soccer player left his sport gracefully than did the aging basketball star.

11. Edgar's younger brother, Speedy, is without a doubt the most laziest person I know.

12. On the charity calendar produced by the Saskatoon Fire Department, it seemed that each month's featured fire fighter was more handsomer than the previous month's.

13. It becomes more and more impossible to find the missing child with each passing day.

14. Heathcliffe was so tired that he could not scarcely get his work done.

15. The Winslows have never done nothing to deserve the incredibly bad luck they've experienced over the past six months.

19.   Misplaced Modifiers

If you have problems completing this exercise, review section 10-7 of *Checkmate: A Writing Reference for Canadians, Third Edition*.

Part 1: Edit the sentences to place the modifiers in the most appropriate places.

EXAMPLE: The pain was so unbearable that I screamed nearly.

REVISED: The pain was so unbearable that I nearly screamed.

a. Ted only told the police officer investigating the accident what he had seen.

b. Barely was the new dormitory finished when we moved in.

c. Some grocery concerns are trying to market cheese products for health-conscious consumers made out of soy.

d. The face of the man peering through the glass sliding door, which was unshaven and menacing, belonged to the cat burglar.

e. People who pursue careers such as daycare assistants become wealthy rarely.

f. Statistics prove that all serious traffic accidents are not caused by drinking and driving; many are caused by drivers talking on cellphones while operating their motor vehicles.

g. It is a by-law infraction to, within municipal boundaries, walk your dog off a leash.

Part 2: The modifiers are awkwardly placed. Edit the paragraphs to improve their clarity and flow.

Lawren Harris, a profound influence on three generations of Canadian painters, was a catalyst in the creation of the Group of Seven. Never has a group such a lasting impact had on the Canadian art scene.

Harris was from a family of great wealth. He went, after attending St. Andrew's College, to the University of Toronto, where he was by his mathematics teacher encouraged to in Berlin study art. In 1908, Harris, upon returning to Canada, went on sketching tours of the Laurentians and the Haliburton area. He drew and painted, at the same time, houses in downtown Toronto.

20. Correcting Dangling Modifiers

If you have problems completing this exercise, review section 10-7E of *Checkmate: A Writing Reference for Canadians, Third Edition.*

Underline any dangling modifiers in the sentences below. Then, rewrite the sentences to correct problems with dangling modifiers. If a sentence has no errors, write "correct" beside it.

> EXAMPLE: After pulling into the driveway, the picket gate slammed shut behind her.
> REVISED: After pulling into the driveway, she slammed the picket gate shut behind her.

1. Partying and playing computer games every day, his marks and reputation as a good student suffered.
2. Our two weeks at the cottage went quickly, swimming and reading mystery novels.
3. To successfully fight a life-threatening disease or injury, determination and family support are required.
4. After visiting the doctor, Jeff's lanced boil completely disappeared.
5. While asleep on the airplane, someone stole my complimentary copy of *Maclean's* magazine.
6. Before arriving for the history seminar, we stopped at the cafeteria for a coffee.
7. The puck, inching across the goal line past the sprawling Red Wing goalie, the crowd at the Air Canada Centre went wild.
8. Travelling through the earthquake-ravaged region, the effects of the devastation became evident.
9. While attending a downtown theatre performance, thieves broke into Ingrid's new Porsche.
10. The tour bus returned to the hotel after dinner was eaten.
11. Keep running until the finish line.
12. Walking near the beach trail, they found the missing old man.

Chapter 11: PUNCTUATION

1.   Commas with Coordinating Conjunctions to Link Independent Clauses, Commas with Compound Elements, and Commas with Introductory Words

If you have problems completing this exercise, review sections 11-1 A, B, and C of *Checkmate: A Writing Reference for Canadians, Third Edition*.

Edit each sentence to correct comma errors. If a sentence has no errors, write "correct" beside it.

1. The weather has turned chilly this September so the leaves in the park have started to change.

2. You can lead a horse to water but you can't make it drink.

3. He paid the bill while Mary collected the coats and they left the Chinese restaurant together.

4. A good chef prepares all the required ingredients and makes sure to wash his or her hands before cooking.

5. When filing for unemployment insurance always bring sufficient identification.

6. Before opening a container of insecticide ensure that you wear rubber gloves.

7. After longer introductory prepositional phrases use a comma to indicate that the main part of the sentence is about to start.

8. While hiking in the Swiss Alps he slipped on the icy surface and fell hundreds of metres to his death.

9. On Fridays I have a beer at the student pub.

10. To verify the real father's identity scientists conducted conclusive DNA testing.

11. By investing wisely in high-return stocks Otto plans to retire midway through his senior year of university.

12. To tell the truth I wish grandpa would quit driving.

2. Commas: In a Series and with Coordinate Adjectives

If you have problems completing this exercise, review sections 11-1 D and E of *Checkmate: A Writing Reference for Canadians, Third Edition*.

Part 1: Commas in a Series
Provide commas where they are needed in the following sentences.

> EXAMPLE: The car swerved veered across the street on two wheels careened off a power pole and plunged down an embankment.
> REVISED: The car swerved, veered across the street on two wheels, careened off a power pole, and plunged down an embankment.

a. The biology slide samples have been sorted, arranged, checked, and labelled.

b. When I have marked your examination paper, when I have tabulated the results, and when I have posted the final score, then you may leave my office.

c. At the family Muskoka resort, we discovered the air is wonderful, the scenery is spectacularly colourful, and the home-cooked meals are divine.

d. I especially enjoy eating around Christmas because at our house one can feast on turkey, stuffing, cranberry sauce, Nuts and Bolts snacks, pate, steak and kidney pie, plum pudding, and Aunt Edith's Christmas cake.

e. Like a true American, he wanted life, liberty, and the pursuit of happiness.

Part 2: Commas with Coordinate Adjectives
Provide commas where they are needed in the following sentences.
(To determine if commas are required, see if the comma can be replaced by *and*.)

a. She was an emotional, brilliant, brutally honest public speaker.

b. Five celebrated Canadian actors attended the party after the play's premiere at the Stratford Festival.

c. I know that Malamutes are large, friendly, playful dogs.

d. The band's greatest hits album featured numerous well-known studio musicians.

e. Getting a university degree or college certificate can be a long, discouraging, expensive process.

f. I woke up to find a sleek, shining, silver Porsche Boxster in my driveway and immediately knew I was still dreaming.

g. He has been a true, dear, faithful friend through the difficult grieving period.

3.   Commas: Setting Off Non-restrictive Elements

If you have problems completing this exercise, review section 11-1F of *Checkmate: A Writing Reference for Canadians, Third Edition*.

Provide commas where they are required. NOTE: Some sentences do not require commas.

1. *A Jest of God* which is my favourite Margaret Laurence book is on Professor Ratke's reading list for the fall semester.

2. Jasmine who has an interest in pottery wants to major in fine arts when she transfers to university.

3. The woman who left the scene of the accident is being sought by every police force in Canada.

4. The robbers with large unmarked bills dangling out of their pockets fled the bank.

5. Dentists offering laser surgery are becoming increasingly common in suburban strip mall offices.

6. The ex-boxer who lost his son to a heroin overdose travels across the country educating young people on the dangers of drug use.

7. Philip Roth's memoir *Patrimony* is the best non-fiction book I've ever read.

8. The Trans-Canada Trail which passes through Burlington is popular among ardent hikers.

9. Donovan Bailey who is arguably the best sprinter that Canada has ever produced won a gold medal at the 1996 Atlanta Olympics.

10. Finally falling asleep Jennifer was soon awoken by a call confirming her Monday appointment at the sleep disorder clinic.

11. His sister who lives in Winnipeg is the one with all the money.

12. The candidate a political lightweight hasn't a hope of winning the election.

4.   General Comma Uses, No. 1

If you have problems completing this exercise, review all of section 11-1 in *Checkmate: A Writing Reference for Canadians, Third Edition.*

Add commas, if they are needed, in the sentences below.

1. Gillian has maintained a 75 percent average throughout her undergraduate studies; however, that academic record will not get her into the prestigious graduate school.

2. He was a very eccentric musician; for example he conducted media interviews while buried up to his neck in sand.

3. In addition he will be tutoring private students.

4. Undoubtedly you will visit us when you pass through Kamloops?

5. Cellphone users I think must consider themselves highly important people.

6. Their popularity waning and their record sales plummeting the band broke up.

7. Royal Roads University not the University of Victoria has an English garden.

8. The Canadian Minister of Foreign Affairs and International Trade unlike her counterpart in Washington issued a statement to the press after the conference.

9. I am writing John to request the article you mentioned in our telephone conversation.

10. Yes you can have a ten-minute coffee break midway through the seminar.

11. You paid your fall tuition installment didn't you?

12. Yeats on the other hand is a very different Irish poet.

5.   General Comma Uses, No. 2

If you have problems completing this exercise, review all of section 11-1 in *Checkmate: A Writing Reference for Canadians, Third Edition*.

Provide commas where they are needed in the sentences below.

1. She said "He would have died anyway."

2. Mom said she will drive to Saskatoon and pick me up for spring break.

3. "It'll stop in due time" he says.

4. "But why" said Jeanne angrily "did you not use Canadian quotations of some sort?"

5. On January 2 1935 Prime Minister R.B. Bennett began a series of live radio broadcasts outlining a "New Deal" for Canada.

6. September 2001 will always be remembered as an especially sad month.

7. Canadian singer and songwriter Sarah McLachlan was born in Halifax Nova Scotia in 1968.

8. Send your tax-deductible contributions to the Me Foundation, care of Me at 2819 Lakeshore Rd. Burlington Ontario L6B 4M1.

9. The musical program at the convocation ceremonies includes The Island Pacific Brass Quintet with Richard Ely Director.

10. An astounding 900 000 people lost their lives when the Chinese river flooded.

11. Beyond the rolling hills continued for kilometres.

12. I'm a lover; Jack a fighter.

6. Avoiding Unnecessary Commas

If you have problems completing this exercise, review section 11-1L of *Checkmate: A Writing Reference for Canadians, Third Edition*.

Some commas are necessary in the sentences below while others are not. Cross out any commas that are not necessary.

1. After staring down the batter, the pitcher wound up, and delivered a mean curve ball.

2. He cannot have hernia surgery, unless he loses weight, and unless he is willing to pay the cost of treatment at a private clinic.

3. As almost every hockey fan knows, Paul Henderson, scored the winning goal for Canada in the 1972 Summit Series.

4. After spring break, the psychology professor returned the marked examinations, to her students.

5. A small number of historians think that, John. A. Macdonald, Mackenzie King, and Pierre Elliot Trudeau, are among the most influential Canadian prime ministers.

6. Confidentially, it was the first, high-stakes, murder investigation on which the rookie detective had worked.

7. Miraculously, it seemed, Sunji completed the exhaustive, biology examination within the allotted, two-hour time period.

8. Our lacrosse players triumphed in the closely, fought contest, and they eventually won the conference championship.

9. The old fire hall, that once was a heritage site, is now, unfortunately, slated for demolition.

10. He said, "Do not park in a space for the handicapped, unless you have an official sticker."

11. In my all-too-rare, leisure hours, I enjoy reading contemporary, humorists such as Steve Martin, Erika Ritter, and David Sedaris.

12. Updating the famous sports saying for a politically correct audience, the sportscaster said that, it is not over until the large-size woman sings.

7.   Comma Review

If you have problems completing this exercise, review all of section 11-1 in *Checkmate: A Writing Reference for Canadians, Third Edition.*

In the following article, some commas are missing, others are incorrectly used, and some are correctly used. Edit the piece, providing necessary commas and eliminating unnecessary ones.

Photographer artist and writer Peter Pitseolak, was born on Nottingham Island Northwest Territories in November of 1902 and he died September, 30 1973. Just before his death Pitseolak said "I am telling the true things I know. I am not adding anything and I am not holding anything back." Pitseolak's passion for telling the truth about his people, produced a stunningly, rich legacy of photographs, paintings, music, and writing. He took his first photograph in the 1930s for a white man who fortunately was too scared to approach a polar bear.

Apparently in the early 1940s while, working for fur traders Pitseolak was given a camera from a Catholic, missionary. Then with help from his wife Ageeok, he developed his very, first photograph in an igloo using a flashlight covered with red cloth.

A leader in his Inuit community Pitseolak realized traditional life was dying so he decided to record its passing by writing diaries notes and manuscripts. As well he drew Inuit customs and legends, and took countless evocative photographs.

Since his death Pitseolak's remarkable photographs have given the world a unique first-hand account of the forces of twentieth-century change on the people of Baffin, Island. During the summer of 2001 a selection from the works of this master storyteller was exhibited at the Canadian Museum of Contemporary Photography.

8.   Semicolon or Comma?

If you have problems completing this exercise, review all of section 11-2 of *Checkmate: A Writing Reference for Canadians, Third Edition.*

Decide whether semicolons or commas are required in the sentences below. Then, circle the correct punctuation within the parentheses. If neither a comma nor a semicolon is required, draw a line through the parentheses.

1. The food at The Rude Waiter Restaurant was superb (, ;) the service was lousy.

2. She was an outstanding athlete (, ;) but her transcripts revealed that she was by no means a scholar.

3. He was the type of employee who was excellent at formulating strategies (, ;) however (, ;) he was not so good at actually carrying them out.

4. Alice Munro employs an oxymoron (, ;) hence (, ;) she underlines the fundamental contradiction in the heroine's predicament.

5. It is wise to plan early for your retirement (, ;) at the same time (, ;) you have to live for today.

6. Having a basic understanding of psychology is invaluable in the workplace (, ;) for example (, ;) it is helpful to know what motivates fellow employees.

7. David is very lineal in his thinking patterns (, ;) while Marcella is a completely divergent thinker.

8. The sports awards dinner was attended by football players, including all of the linebackers (, ;) a defensive back (, ;) and the split ends (, ;) basketball players, including the centre (, ;) a point guard (, ;) and the water person (, ;) and hockey players, such as the goalie (, ;) her backup (, ;) and two forwards.

9. Our reading list in English 134.5 was rich in Canadian novels and included (, ;) *Barney's Version* (, ;) *In the Skin of a Lion* (, ;) and *The Honorary Patron.*

10. Once the student painters had finished painting the living room (, ;) they moved on to the dining room.

11. Stephano would not miss an episode of *The Sopranos* (, ;) a dark (, ;) but well-written and finely acted portrayal of the life of an extended mob family.

12. In conclusion (, ;) the Nanaimo Estuary is a rich and vital ecosystem (, ;) that residents cannot afford to lose.

9. Editing for Correct Comma and Semicolon Use

If you have problems completing this exercise, review all of sections 11-1 and 11-2 in *Checkmate: A Writing Reference for Canadians, Third Edition*.

Part 1: Provide needed commas and semicolons.

c. In theory the mayor's office can do a lot to ease the housing crisis in practice it can do very little.

i. Canadian Prime Minister Arthur Meighen once said "Inflation makes misery unanimous it is universal poverty."

j. Winning is not only a good thing it is the only thing.

k. In the Edmonton Oilers' glory years the team featured Mark Messier a hard-nosed centre Glenn Anderson an incredibly fast skater and Wayne Gretzky thought by many to be the best player to lace on a pair of skates.

l. To paraphrase Woody Allen death doesn't scare me I just don't want to be there when it happens.

Part 2: If needed, add commas or semicolons within the parentheses. If no punctuation is needed, leave the parentheses empty.

Lester Bowles "Mike" Pearson ( ) (1897–1972) was an athlete ( ) war veteran ( ) history professor ( ) and gifted diplomat. His contributions to Canada are significant. Pearson served on Parliament Hill as prime minister from 1963 to 1968 ( ) established the National Arts Centre ( ) proposed the first UN peacekeeping force to address the volatile 1956 Suez Crisis ( ) commemorated at The Peacekeeping Monument ( ) and gave us our national flag ( ) many thousands of which now fly throughout our country. Pearson headed the Department of External Affairs from 1946 ( ) after its tremendous wartime expansion under the brilliant Norman Robertson. As a politician ( ) Pearson continued to use his diplomatic talents to make Canada a major partner in the new UN and NATO ( ) in essence ( ) he played a major role in developing Canada's world peacekeeping reputation. His 1957 Nobel Peace Prize medal is displayed in the main lobby of the Lester B. Pearson Building ( ) headquarters of the Department of Foreign Affairs and International Trade.

10.   Correct Colon Use

If you have problems completing this exercise, review all of section 11-3 in *Checkmate: A Writing Reference for Canadians, Third Edition*.

Edit the sentences below to place the colon in the correct place. You may need to replace a comma or semicolon. In a few sentences, no colons are required.

1. There are four kinds of men on campus the handsome, the intelligent, the rich, and all the rest.

2. Pierre Elliot Trudeau said it best "The army is a poor training corps for democracy, no matter how inspiring the cause."

3. One policy dominates the president's foreign policy on Iraq regime change.

4. When you are somewhat agitated, squeeze the cuddly stress doll; when you are extremely agitated, cleave it with an axe.

5. Dear Dr. Liverwitz

    I am writing to apply for the veterinary assistant position recently advertised in *The Globe and Tail* …

6. A minute of silence will be observed at 8 39 a. m. to honour the memory of the victims.

7. Despite his barren love life, he felt optimistic about his chances of getting a date, since the ratio of women to men in the community college was 8 1.

8. The core textbook for the sociology course is *The Challenge of Diversity Multiculturalism in Canada*.

9. Hill, Lawrence. *Black Berry, Sweet Juice On Being Black and White in Canada*. Toronto HarperCollins, 2001.

10. Some major causes of heart attacks are bad diet, stress, lack of exercise, and smoking.

11. E.J. Pratt's "Towards the Last Spike" appears in *Literature in Canada Volume 2*.

12. The proposed residence for senior students had many attractive features, such as microwave ovens, DVD players, and full bathrooms in every suite.

11.   Comma, Semicolon, or Colon?

If you have problems completing this exercise, review all of sections 11-1, 11-2, and 11-3 in *Checkmate: A Writing Reference for Canadians, Third Edition*.

The memorandum below has no commas, semicolons, or colons. Edit it by providing the correct punctuation.

Memo

To	All Fitness Consultants
From	Jeff Hackett Marketing Manager Family Fitness Corporation
Subject	Members Wearing Tank Tops While Working Out
Copy	Ms. Marion Wurlizter Executive President
	Mr. Corky Weisner Executive Vice President
Date	October 5 2006

As we discussed in our last meeting there are too many patrons working out on exercise equipment while wearing tank tops the practice cannot continue. First this presents an extremely odious hygiene risk and it could cause problems for us should health inspectors visit our premises. Third Family Fitness Corporation wishes to present itself as a family-oriented fitness club therefore having predominantly young scantily clad and often steroid-enhanced bodybuilders on display does nothing to foster the Disney-like image we would like to project. Washboard abdominals bulging pectorals and rippling quads can be intimidating to the overweight general public. At present we have a ratio of family memberships to young singles of 3 to 1 and I want very much to increase the number of family memberships.

I would like to convene a meeting for Thursday August 10 2007 at 10 30 a.m. to discuss the issue. Some topics we might discuss include the following what constitutes a tank top particularly how much sleeve remnant officially constitutes one how do we communicate the policy perhaps by dropping leaflets from passing airliners and how do we enforce such a policy maybe by hiring a S.W.A.T. team of tank-top police.
Please make note of your ideas relating to this pressing issue and let me know if the appointed time is convenient for you otherwise I will have to book a different room. I look forward to seeing you at the meeting properly attired of course!

Jeff Hackett

12.   Correct Use of the Apostrophe

If you have problems completing this exercise, review all of section 11-4 in *Checkmate: A Writing Reference for Canadians, Third Edition*.

Correct any errors in apostrophe use. If the apostrophe is correctly used, place a check mark above it. In a few instances, needed apostrophes are missing.

1. The students' laptop was left on a table when he went to the men's washroom.

2. Despite his parents' darkest worries, the job Jason wanted was right behind destinys' door.

3. The Wilsons' attended the Flames' game at Calgary's famous Saddledome.

4. The women's book fair will be held at the presidents' home after Thursdays' budget meeting.

5. Grant's and Joanne's garden is now in full and glorious bloom.

6. In terms of elegance, the McLeod and the Rappenport's cottages are like night and day.

7. Bess' most outstanding feature, according to her father, is her paternal grandmothers' Slavic nose.

8. Julians' brother was difficult to work with and constantly argued that his job duties were someone elses' responsibility.

9. Did you know that Maury's brother-in-laws' law firm is handling the mayors' highly confidential paternity suit?

10. In Damians' opinion, the crows'-nests' of tall ships are the best places to view the harbour.

11. Its anyones' guess who won't attend the kids' high school reunion.

12. Whos' planning to audit our local M.L.A.s' exorbitant expense claims?

13.   Correct Use of Quotation Marks and Using Punctuation with Quotation Marks

If you have problems completing this exercise, review all of section 11-5 in *Checkmate: A Writing Reference for Canadians, Third Edition.*

Part 1: Provide needed quotation marks. Not all sentences need them.

a. As Albert Einstein said, Great souls will always encounter violent opposition from mediocre minds.

b. Wimpy always said that he would gladly pay you Thursday for a hamburger today.

c. Military intelligence is a contradiction in terms, said Groucho Marx.

d. In describing what sort of future the aging population will bring, David K. Foote states, writer Nicholas Kristoff offer[s] a gloomy view … of conflict between a minority of working young and a majority of retired 'greedy geezers.'

e. Alice Munro's vision of the contradictory nature of love is brilliantly rendered in her short story Dulce.

f. The mischievous journalist bet a colleague that he could naturally weave the phrase bodacious yams into one of his feature sports articles.

Part 2: Correct any errors in the placement of quotation marks or accompanying punctuation.

a. "To tell you the truth", says Uncle George slowly ",your father was a crook."

b. I'll give you my personal definition of the term "previously owned automobile:" an expensive clunker.

c. The chief economist termed the trend an "inflationary spiral;" however, the Statistics Canada data did not support this view.

d. "Where are you staying"? Tony asks politely, meaning, when are you leaving.

e. Marie Winn presents an opposing view ": The self-confessed television addict often feels he ought to do other things but the fact he does not read or have conversations means that those activities are no longer as desirable as television viewing".

f. According to the newspaper, the mobster testified at his trial that, "he was not the only one."

14.   Using Other Punctuation Marks Correctly

If you have problems completing this exercise, review all of section 11-6 in *Checkmate: A Writing Reference for Canadians, Third Edition.*

Part 1: Supply periods, question marks, or exclamation points where needed.

a.   The coach asked us if we had it in us to win the game

b.   Please turn on your computer

c.   She will attend the convocation ceremonies when she completes all the requirements for her M B A

d.   Will there be anything about the major Elizabethan dramatists on the examination

e.   Run, I think the house is on fire

f.   For your research on Canadian broadcasting, will you visit the CBC station in Edmonton, AB Maybe the headquarters in Toronto, ON Or, perhaps it would be a good idea to tour the studio in Halifax, NS

Part 2: Use dashes, parentheses, or square brackets to correctly set off the underlined information.

a) Sir Frances Bacon <u>correctly, as we now know</u> realized that science could provide as much wonder as any magician with a wand.

b) Within the invisible <u>yet perceptible</u> walls of the barrio are several people living in too few houses.

c) Yet the serious writing students can learn much from the piece <u>not only from its minor faults but also from its many strengths as a descriptive essay.</u>

d) The trouble with King Henry <u>Henry VIII</u> was that he had a mind of his own and an eye for the ladies.

e) The Alabama magazine reported that Toronto <u>*sic*</u> is the capital of Canada.

f) We should agree that global ecological catastrophes <u>such as global warming, ozone depletion, and acid rain</u> are mostly caused by OECD countries' oil, mining, timber, and heavy manufacturing conglomerates.

Chapter 12: *Sentence Structure and Style*

1.   Avoiding Awkward Sentence Shifts

If you have problems completing this exercise, review section 12-1 of *Checkmate: A Writing Reference for Canadians, Third Edition*.

Edit the sentence to eliminate any shifts in point of view, verb tense, mood, voice, or direct to indirect discourse. If a sentence has no errors, write "correct" beside it.

EXAMPLE: Anne always booked into Comfortable Inns since she finds they took pets.

REVISED: Anne always booked into Comfortable Inns since she **found** they took pets.

1. Ted was terrified while driving along the black-ice-coated 401 Expressway, for one saw everywhere the carnage and wreckage from previous motor vehicle accidents.

2. When you want to avoid the risk of mutual funds in an uncertain stock market, we purchase Canada Savings Bonds.

3. Fifthly, Shakespeare alters the way in which Iago got possession of the handkerchief.

4. Angelee raced to answer the telephone, but nobody is on the line.

5. During the long drive to the cottage, Sal told stories about his glory days as a rugby player while his girlfriend sleeps soundly.

6. I want to meet the manager when employment statistics are improving and companies will be hiring.

7. Address the chairperson first, and then you will be acknowledged.

8. She detested dishonesty, and by her standards, all hypocrites were considered offensive.

9. At Blue Jays' games, it is an important part of a ticket taker's responsibilities to collect tickets from paying customers and don't let any gatecrashers into the stadium.

10. If I were wealthy and Tony was here, we would immediately go to the student pub to imbibe our favourite beverage.

11. While travelling in Europe, I asked a local resident which road do you take to get to the cathedral?

12. She replied, "Take this road to where the old rectory used to be and turn left."

2.   Mixed Constructions

If you have problems completing this exercise, review section 12-2 of *Checkmate: A Writing Reference for Canadians, Third Edition*.

Rewrite each sentence to correct any mixed constructions.

EXAMPLE: The reason for the new library loan policy was implemented to ensure all students have access to needed research materials.

REVISED: The new library loan policy was implemented to ensure all students have access to needed research materials.

1. By increasing the amount of time she devoted to studying anthropology raised Elsa's mark two letter grades for the spring semester.

   _____

   _____

2. After completing a rigorous program in microbiology it was at an Ontario institution, Garrett pursued his medical studies at a leading university in the Maritimes.

   _____

   _____

3. Because the explorers could not locate an entrance to the Northwest Passage, so they abandoned their expedition.

   _____

   _____

4. News of the final cuts for the varsity field hockey team was made by the coach to each affected player.

   _____

   _____

5. Bungee jumping, people with more money than brains, can have tragic consequences if proper safety precautions are not taken.

   _____

   _____

6. Almonte, Ontario, is where the inventor of basketball, a physician and educator, James A. Naismith was born.

   _____

   _____

7. Because Daphne was half an hour late was the reason we missed the rap concert.

   _____

   _____

8. The water tower, I saw it from the cockpit of the glider.

   _____

   _____

3.   Using Coordination and Subordination to Fix Choppy Sentences

If you have problems completing this exercise, review section 12-3A of *Checkmate: A Writing Reference for Canadians, Third Edition.*

Rewrite the following paragraphs using subordination and coordination to eliminate choppy sentences. Note that there are a number of acceptable alternatives.

1. William Maxwell (Max) Aitken is also known as 1st Baron Beaverbook. He was financier, politician, author, and publisher. Beaverbrook was the son of a minister. He would later claim that his religious beliefs were the foundation of his success. Aitken moved with his family to New Brunswick in 1880. He was a bright if not mischievous youth. The young Aitken showed a great love for acquiring money. He tried journalism. He sold insurance. Then, Aitken worked as a legal clerk in Chatham, New Brunswick. At this job, he began a lifelong friendship with R.B. Bennett. Bennett later became prime minister of Canada. In 1897, Max left law school to follow Bennett to Calgary. In Calgary, Aitken operated a bowling alley. Then, he moved to Edmonton. Finally, he returned to the Maritimes.

2. Eating is an important part of a sumo wrestler's preparation. Most wrestlers weigh more than 136 kg. Much of the weight is concentrated in their stomach and hips. This area generates the pushing power so important in sumo wrestling. The extra mass also acts as a shock absorber. It allows a wrestler to stay on his feet in spite of his opponent's efforts to topple him. Do not dismiss sumo wrestlers as slow, fat food addicts. Sumo wrestlers have enormous size. They also possess agility, strength, speed, and balance.

3. There are three major stages in the process of making a good instructional video. The first stage is *pre-production.* In pre-production students plan their videos on paper. Pre-production involves all the planning. This continues until the day students take out the camera. Students are in the *production* stage when they handle the equipment. *Post-production* is the final stage. It involves pulling all the shots together. Post-production also involves making sense of the video footage.

4. In the 1920s, investigators realized that it was the chromosomes that carried the genes and information of heredity. Much later, in 1953, a major breakthrough occurred in chemistry. James Watson and Frances Crick discovered the DNA (deoxyribonucleic acid) molecule. They did this working in Cambridge. This discovery disclosed the fundamental mechanism of how heredity really worked.

4.   Effective Coordination and Subordination

If you have problems completing this exercise, review all of section 12-3 in *Checkmate: A Writing Reference for Canadians, Third Edition*.

Edit the sentences to correct any coordination or subordination problems. There may be more than one acceptable alternative.

EXAMPLE: In 1970–71, Ken Dryden played only 6 regular-season games in the NHL, and he played the entire playoffs for the Montreal Canadiens.

REVISED: In 1970–71, after only 6 regular-season games in the NHL, Ken Dryden played the entire playoffs for the Montreal Canadiens.

1. Electronic mail is an excellent tool for international communication, and people responding to messages sometimes inadvertently transmit computer viruses.

2. Television is one technology that most Canadians have in common, and almost all of Canada's 12 million households have televisions sets (99%), so this is more than households that own automobiles (60%) and home computers (75%).

3. Unfortunately, the driver died at the scene of the accident, and there were many well-equipped paramedics attending to her.

4. The prison guard noticed that the convict's bunk was empty and sounded the alarm that a prison break had occurred.

5. I was wearing my insulated vest and looking through high-powered binoculars, while I observed the unidentified flying object.

6. While there are a number of procedures to follow, if you think you have been discriminated against or harassed by someone in your workplace.

7. The Raptor's power forward was a rookie in the NBA, although he had a better understanding of the game than many veteran players.

8. Recently, the provincial government deregulated electricity prices, and the cost to consumers skyrocketed, and the governing party will pay dearly for the policy change when voters go to the polls in the next election.

9. While dieting can have many benefits, if you do it without consulting your doctor, when trying to lose significant amounts of weight, since you can deprive yourself of essential nutrients, it can pose significant health risks.

10. The movie, which is my favourite that the Italian director, who is in his prime, has done since emigrating to America, won an Academy Award.

5.   Parallelism

If you have problems completing this exercise, review section 12-4 of *Checkmate: A Writing Reference for Canadians, Third Edition.*

Revise each sentence to correct any parallelism problems.

EXAMPLE: Home renovators face demanding problems estimating costs and in keeping conscientious employees.

REVISED: Home renovators face demanding problems in estimating costs and in keeping conscientious employees.

1. The new geography instructor has eloquence, charm, warmth, humour, a breadth of subject knowledge, and he is an outstanding teacher.

2. *My Big Fat Greek Wedding* was funny, touching, well acted, intelligent, and enjoyed by those who viewed the movie.

3. Our literature study group discussed, analyzed, questioned, and then wrote a paraphrase of sections of Earle Birney's *David.*

4. The corporate executive faced his trial confidently, insisting that he was innocent and he rejected any offers of a plea bargain.

5. The sprinter won the European championship by intimidating her opponents and she used steroids.

6. The lawyer tried to bait witnesses with seemingly innocent questions and then she would expose inconsistencies in their testimony.

7. The prime minister spoke to the grieving relatives of the victims with unquestionable sincerity and resolution to seek justice.

8. Thomas Hobbes, a pessimist, thought that life was "nasty, brutish, and short" and he saw every man as having a price.

9. A good after-dinner speaker must be confident and display a good sense of humour.

10. The RCMP not only accused the district manager of embezzlement but also the company president.

11. Dilbert may not have been the prettiest car in the parking lot, but it is more reliable than any of the other cars parked there.

12. One can pay by cash, Visa, Mastercard, or the consumer has the option of using Interac.

6.   Needed Words

If you have problems completing this exercise, review section 12-5 of *Checkmate: A Writing Reference for Canadians, Third Edition.*

Edit each sentence by supplying any missing word or words. If a sentence has no errors, write "correct" beside it.

EXAMPLE: Show examples of concrete objects mathematics students could create.

REVISED: Show examples of concrete objects that mathematics students could create.

1. The rookie defenceman's salary is meagre compared to the all-star centre.

2. The Toronto Maple Leafs have a larger fan base than any sports team in the Ontario capital.

3. Vancouver has a larger population of sailboat owners than any city in Alberta.

4. Margaret Atwood's work is more widely recognized than any other Canadian writer.

5. Canada is as well regarded, and no doubt more so, than any other nation contributing peacekeeping forces to the region.

6. The youngest dog runs for kilometres while the older dogs for mere metres.

7. The university's chancellor is aware and in agreement with the proposal to create a memorial garden.

8. The young racer's skis are as well polished as an Olympic champion.

9. We saw the movie, which was garnering outstanding reviews, was completely sold out.

10. The scholarship student spends countless hours studying, but other scholarship students less time.

11. The local company has always and will continue to promote from within.

12. Mother gave her more praise than you.

7.   Creating Sentence Variety

If you have problems completing this exercise, review section 12-6 of *Checkmate: A Writing Reference for Canadians, Third Edition.*

Use strategies you learned in *Checkmate* to provide improved sentence variety in the passage below.

Glenn Gould, a musical virtuoso, is best known for his brilliant and innovative interpretations of classical piano compositions. Many people do not appreciate that he had a remarkably varied creative career. His career spanned recording, writing, producing radio documentaries, composing, and conducting.

Gould was born in Toronto. He lived there all his life. He was only three years old when he demonstrated exceptional music abilities such as perfect pitch. Gould was soon playing his own compositions for family and friends. He then competed in a few music festivals. His parents carefully nurtured his talent. They never subjected him to the life of a star prodigy. Gould's mother was his only music teacher until he was ten. He then began lessons at the Royal Conservatory of Music in Toronto. Gould studied organ, piano, and music theory. He was awarded a diploma with highest honours in 1946, at age 14. His first public piano recital was in 1947. It included works by the composers Scarlatti, Beethoven, Chopin, and Liszt.

Glenn Gould was known across Canada by the early 1950s. This was a result of his concert appearances, CBC radio and television broadcasts, and recordings.

He made his American debut in 1955 in Washington and then New York. The recitals included an unconventional program of composers. His performances were dazzling. He was signed to a recording contract the day after the New York appearance. His interpretation of J.S. Bach's *Goldberg Variations* was released in 1956. The recording, his first, received critical and popular acclaim. It became the best-selling classical record of 1956.

8.   Effective Sentences Review

If you have problems completing this exercise, review section 12-6 of *Checkmate: A Writing Reference for Canadians, Third Edition.*

Correct any shifts in voice, mood, or tense, and provide improved sentence variety in the passage below.

During his lifetime, Grey Owl was a trapper, author, imposter, and he had visionary ideas about conservation. Arguably, he did more to promote conservation in Canada than any Canadian during the first half of the twentieth century.

Grey Owl's real name was Archibald Stansfield Belaney. He was born in 1888. He was born in Hastings, England. Archie was fascinated with North American Natives as a boy.

Belaney sailed to Canada as soon as he was old enough to travel. He lived with the Ojibwa of northern Ontario, and he learned about the wilderness and soon began presenting himself as the son of a Scot and an Apache.

Though he lied about his Native heritage, all of his presentations were not fabrication. Grey Owl, his Native name, sincerely worked for preservation of the beaver and their sensitive habitats. For example, he kept two beaver called Jelly Roll and Rawhide at his northern Ontario home. However, he later moved west. In 1931, Grey Owl boarded a westbound train with Jelly Roll and Rawhide—travelling to Manitoba's Riding Mountain National Park and a cabin that is built especially for him on the shore of Beaver Lodge Lake.

Grey Owl also nurtured his writing career and made speaking tours to Europe. By posing as a Native person during a time when Europeans held romantic images of Canada's first peoples, he found his ideas about protecting the environment will be better received.

After the press discovered his English birth and headlines such as the following appeared: "GREY OWL HAD COCKNEY ACCENT AND FOUR WIVES," Grey Owl's death in 1938.

9.   Wordiness: Eliminating Redundancies, Avoiding Unnecessary Repetition, and Cutting Empty or Inflated Phrases

If you have problems completing this exercise, review section 12-7 of *Checkmate: A Writing Reference for Canadians, Third Edition*.

In questions 1-10, edit each sentence to eliminate redundancies or unnecessary repetition. In question 11, edit the short passage to replace all empty or inflated phrases.

> EXAMPLE: The construction company is in close proximity to reaching the final completion date for the innovative new bridge.
>
> REVISION: The construction company is close to reaching the completion date for the innovative bridge.

1. The company vice president must catch an 8:30 p.m. evening flight from the Vancouver airport.
2. At the meeting, he had a very unique proposal but presented it in a soft voice, so he was asked to repeat it again.
3. The circular-shaped pool was not good for swimming laps.
4. In summary, I conclude from past experience that mutual cooperation is the most basic requirement of any successful team.
5. In this day and age, it is unique to find someone who has the ability to write so eloquently and understand modern telecommunications technology so profoundly.
6. The reason that many working people voted for Richard Nixon in the 1972 election was because his tax plan still allowed them to realize the American dream.
7. The lumbering octopus with eight tentacles slowly swam past the eel.
8. She always consistently championed the fundamental and basic principles of free speech and personal freedom.
9. Essentially, for all intents and purposes, the Montreal Expos are a threatened, if not near dead and almost extinct, baseball franchise.
10. Being that Quan is the only surviving relative, he will inherit in the order of two million dollars on the occasion of his great uncle's unfortunate demise.
11. Because of the fact that the rotating home has a unique design and materials, it is in the neighbourhood of 30 percent more energy efficient than traditional homes. This is in the event you do not turn the home. In the event that you use the house to its full rotation potential, and track the sun, it will be even more energy efficient. As a matter of fact, dome homes at the present time in Europe have been hooked up with solar panels, and a few even use computers in order to track the sun and maximize solar-power potential. Such computer-controlled solar heating systems in addition allow windows to collect passive solar heat. In the summer, the computer turns the home away from the sun.

10.   Eliminating Empty or Inflated Phrases

If you have problems completing this exercise, review section 12-7C of *Checkmate: A Writing Reference for Canadians, Third Edition.*

Part 1: Edit the sentences by eliminating any empty or inflated phrases.

EXAMPLE: The essay should be along the lines of the poetry analysis students completed prior to Christmas and be in the neighbourhood of 800 words.

REVISION: The essay should be ~~along the lines of~~ **similar to** the poetry analysis students completed ~~prior to~~ **before** Christmas and be ~~in the neighbourhoo~~ **about** 800 words.

a. Following discussions between representatives of the regional offices and central administrative services, senior management has come to the conclusion that downsizing is not a viable option at the present time.

b. She will not undertake business travel outside the country because of the fact that her father is battling a serious illness.

c. In order to advance within the organization, a manager must have the ability to delegate responsibility and write coherent memoranda.

d. Due to the fact that we have recently implemented an enhancement to our computer system that will enable us to provide better service to our valued customers, there has been a slight delay with regard to the processing of your refund.

e. The lawyer has said time and again that all she has ever wanted is a settlement that would provide for the economic security of the families in order to pay for her client's medical bills in the future to come.

f. In the event that her unemployment insurance entitlement expires, she will secure temporary employment until such a time as she manages to find a position in the field for which she was trained.

g. He was able to obtain work as a floral delivery person in spite of the fact that he had a driving conviction by virtue of the fact that he was operating a motor vehicle at two times the legal limit of alcohol.

h. As a matter of fact, behavioural research shows that ducks have a tendency to quack in the event that they are disturbed by humans.

i. In a manner of speaking, they have exceeded the deadline, but they are in the process of completing the required work in an expeditious manner.

j. It seems that, in the final analysis, university was not the best option in view of the fact that she likes to imbibe and fraternize with fellow students.

Part 2: Edit the passage to make it clear, concise, and direct.

We have reviewed the fundamental principles of the admissions policy and concluded that, due to the fact that more candidates are applying for entrance than we currently have space, it will be incumbent upon us, as administrators, to increase the minimum acceptable academic standard. This policy will be implemented until such a time as the volume of applications subsides in order that administrative personnel in Admissions can process them in a timely manner. The new admissions policy will go into effect on the occasion of the spring deadline for applications for the upcoming semester. In the final analysis, the aforementioned was our only viable option.

11.   Simplify Sentence Structure/Revise Wordy Sentences

If you have problems completing this exercise, review section 12-7D of *Checkmate: A Writing Reference for Canadians, Third Edition.*

Edit each sentence below to simplify structure and reduce wordiness.

EXAMPLE: The baby was found by the neighbour's boy, who is ten years old. REVISION: The neighbour's ten-year-old boy found the baby.

1. Petra's failure to submit assignments on time was an indication of her poor learning attitude.

2. The rescue workers were making slow advancement towards the trapped miners, and the minimal progress was troublesome to doctors who were concerned about the victims' physical and mental health.

3. It is a secret dream of Brian to live a life like Hugh Hefner's.

4. There are many opportunities that you have to do make-up assignments and improve your final biology mark.

5. It is a hope of my mother that I will continue my study of Canadian literature in graduate school.

6. An independent research firm was commissioned by the federal government to conduct an extensive study of the physical fitness of college and university students in Canada.

7. I was taught by my father never to gulp wine and eat peas with a butter knife at expensive restaurants, especially when he was paying the bill.

8. My wallet was stolen by a thief wearing a burgundy coat and jeans.

9. The road from Wiarton to Tobermory, which is 90 kilometres in length, passes through a reserve, where many of the residents are Ojibway.

10. Full of confidence, Marcie entered the room in which the job interview was held.

11. The point guard, who was an all-star, cocked her wrist and successfully shot the basket, which won the conference title game in the dying seconds.

12. The chemist, who has won a Nobel Prize and is known all around the world, will speak in the lecture theatre, which can accommodate five hundred people.

Chapter 13: *Usage*

1.   Appropriate Language: Avoiding Jargon, Pretentious Language, and Euphemisms

If you have problems completing this exercise, review sections 13-1 A and B of *Checkmate: A Writing Reference for Canadians, Third Edition*.

Edit each sentence, replacing any jargon, pretentious language, and euphemisms.

EXAMPLE: All elementary reading at-risk students should be encouraged to practise metacognition and regular journalling.

REVISED: All elementary students who are having reading difficulties should be encouraged to reflect on their learning and to write in their journals regularly.

1. His raison d'etre was to pen avant-garde poetry, and when he encountered a compatible femme fatale, a meaningful relationship was a fait accompli.

2. Since Enid is facing a cash-flow dilemma, she has downsized by purchasing a pre-owned automobile.

3. The hostile forces accomplished pacification of the area with minimal collateral damage and then made a strategic withdrawal.

4. They finalized judging on *American Idol* by prioritizing candidates according to pre-established talent parameters and in due course selected the optimal contestant.

5. The vertically challenged, hearing-impaired golden-ager has, forthwith, gone to the great beyond.

6. Today, the victims of the terrorist incendiary devices were laid to rest in a memorial garden.

7. Bob, an alpha-geek, was particularly sensitive to angry, fruit salad designs on websites.

8. Ed McDougal of our Winnipeg office will liaise with our management committee on optimal strategies for growing our business in the present bear-market economy.

9. The waste disposal technician endeavoured to ameliorate the overabundance of liquid in the porcelain receptacle by using a dome-shaped rubber suction device.

2. Appropriate Language: Avoiding Slang, Regional Expressions, and Informal Language

If you have problems completing this exercise, review section 13-1 C and D of *Checkmate: A Writing Reference for Canadians, Third Edition*.

Edit the following letter to replace any slang, regional expressions, or informal language with appropriate language.

1412 Prince Dr.
Markham, ON M3H 2L4

November 12, 2011

Harry Wong
Executive Director
Alliance of Part-time Undergraduate Students
27 Wellesley St., Room 362
Toronto, Ontario   M5S 1A9

Dear Harry,
I am writing because I really, really want that research position advertised on www.wowjob.ca.

Over the past three plus years, I have sweated my buns off as a researcher for various education profs. at the U. of Waterloo. A humungous part of my work involved assisting various profs. in their research to determine which teaching strategies and materials are used within the educational community. I was the go-to gal for administering research surveys and questionnaires by mail, telephone, and e-mail. To boot, I proofread final analysis reports, gaining a reputation as one demon editor. My work often required ringing up big honchos at schools, school board offices, colleges, universities, and departments of education.

I have also helped conduct market analysis research projects in the biz world. A recent project I worked on involved surveying telecommunications decision makers to get a fix on their customer needs.

While a summer intern with the B.C. Ministry of Education, I helped file in the Assessment Branch.

My writing skills are tops. To give you just one example, this past academic year, I copped a prize for the best undergraduate essay, and I have published two short stories in the campus rag.

I'd love to drop by your office for a chat over a cup of Joe and tell you all about my qualifications.
Chow for now,

Enc.
cc Professor Edward Bennie

3.   Avoiding Sexist Language

If you have problems completing this exercise, review section 13-1E of *Checkmate: A Writing Reference for Canadians, Third Edition*.

Rewrite each sentence below to eliminate problems with sexist language.

EXAMPLE: Gwen is enjoying her course in freshman English.

REVISED: Gwen is enjoying her course in ~~freshman~~ first-year English.

1.   The female alderman threatens to sue anyone who even suggests she might be influenced in her voting patterns by male developers.

2.   Mr. John Seymour Hilderbrant III, Q.C., and his attractive young wife, Cookie, were among the honoured guests at the head table of the charity ball.

3.   Just like all men, he refuses to listen when I want to discuss our relationship.

4.   Anyone wanting to compete in the 10 K event must bring his entry form and fee to the recreation centre office by Thursday at 4 p.m.

5.   The boys hadn't seen each other for years and talked like a couple of old women.

6.   The project editor is responsible for ensuring that each contributing author completes his chapter by the appointed deadline.

7.   Please give each registrant a certificate as soon as she completes the course.

8.   The typical college student is concerned about the steadily rising cost of his tuition.

9.   If any student is dissatisfied with the fairness of a paper's grading, he can have it reviewed by a faculty ombudsman.

10. As he progresses in his studies, the graduate student specializes in his field of study.

11. The veteran newsman regretted that his newspaper didn't have the manpower to adequately cover school board issues.

12. Mr. Singh was furious when the mailman took the parcel intended for the courier despite the fact he had posted a note telling her not to do so.

4. Improving Sentences: Exact Language, Concrete Nouns, and Active Verbs

If you have problems completing this exercise, review section 13-2 A, B, and C of *Checkmate: A Writing Reference for Canadians, Third Edition.*

Edit each sentence to improve the writer's use of language. If a sentence does not need any changes, write "correct" beside it.

EXAMPLE: His clunker was parked next to a local building.

REVISED: He parked his older model car next to City Hall.

1. It was our first vacation to a Third World country, and we found the capital city was overrun with vagrants.

2. The snotty neighbour snitched to a by-law officer every time the old wench's mutt barked.

3. The small house had a plot full of different flowers.

4. There were several aspects of the survey that yielded good results and will need to be considered in future.

5. After hitting the meridian, the car slid along the wet passing lane as the driver turned significantly to just avoid a stalled cement truck.

6. A compelling speech on forgiveness was given by Nobel laureate Desmond Tutu.

7. Death is an unpopular topic at the dinner table.

8. Denying a political prisoner access to a lawyer is a violation of his or her legal rights.

9. The soldiers inside the fort were intrigued by the new sport, so the gates were opened and they watched Chief Pontiac and the Ottawas play lacrosse.

10. The entire team is quitting.

11. Donald was assured by his doctor that the results of the medical test were accurate.

12. The record-setting home-run ball was hit out of the park by the centre fielder, and millions of dollars paid by the wealthy cartoonist for the previous record-setting ball went with it.

5.   Using Standard Idioms

If you have problems completing this exercise, review section 13-2D of *Checkmate: A Writing Reference for Canadians, Third Edition.*

Edit each sentence below to make it idiomatically correct.

   EXAMPLE: She is angry at her father for cancelling her credit cards.

   REVISED: She is angry **with** her father for cancelling her credit cards.

1. I intend on doing my income tax when I receive all of my T-4 slips from my previous employer.

2. Desmond told me to be sure and include a bibliography with the history assignment.

3. Bruce Springsteen is different than all the other aging rock stars playing the Air Canada Centre this fall.

4. Get that dog off of the sofa!

5. The teaching assistant recommended her to do a prerequisite course in cellular biology.

6. The student painters accepted to do the entire living room for $400.

7. Calvin filed an insurance claim of $200 in reference to the damage sustained during the flood of 2000.

8. You must comply to the posted speed limits, especially in school zones.

9. Having linoleum or hardwood as flooring is preferable than shag carpeting when one has dogs that spend a lot of time in the basement.

10. I will suggest him to do the work immediately.

11. His batting stance was superior than that of any other player on the minor league team.

12. The retirement party will culminate with a version of "For He's a Jolly Good Fellow."

13. Melvyn was associated to the notorious motorcycle gang Satan's Geezers

14. Shelley was the type of a mother who would do anything for her children.

6. Avoiding Clichés and Mixed Metaphors

If you have problems completing this exercise, review section 13-2 E and F of *Checkmate: A Writing Reference for Canadians, Third Edition.*

Part 1: Underline the cliché; then, write the sentence without a cliché.

EXAMPLE: In one fell swoop, all district managers were fired.

REVISED: In one fell swoop **Suddenly,** all district managers were fired.

a. The cyclist was already dead as a doornail when the officer arrived at the scene of the accident.

b. At the athletic banquet, the linebacker went straight as an arrow to the buffet table where prime rib was being served.

c. With any wedding, the responsibility of the master of ceremonies is first and foremost to remember the names of the bride and groom.

d. The socialist, bilingual bookstore is for all intents and purposes bankrupt.

e. It was a step in the right direction when the government appointed a local parent to oversee cuts in the school board budget.

Part 2: Underline the mixed metaphors; then, write the sentence with effective figurative language.

EXAMPLE: I'm worried about my roommate because she has been burning the midnight oil at both ends.

REVISED: I'm worried about my roommate because she has been burning the midnight oil at both ends **burning the candle at both ends**.

a. By cheating on the examination you've buttered your bread, so now you must lie in it.

b. If you start complaining about dormitory noise when you're not the quietest person yourself, you'll be opening a whole Pandora's box of worms.

c. According to our physical education instructor, a sound mind and a sound body go hand in hand.

d. When it comes to completing an essay on time, you just have to grab the bull by the horns and run with it.

e. The eccentric impressionist painter marched to the beat of a dead duck.

Chapter 14: *Mechanics and Spelling*

1.　　Spelling, No. 1

If you have problems completing this exercise, review section 14-1 A, B, and C of *Checkmate: A Writing Reference for Canadians, Third Edition*.
The sentences contain errors that break spelling rules, misuse homophones, and display common spelling mistakes. Edit the sentences to correct all spelling errors.

　　EXAMPLE: I have absolutly no allusions about my incredable inteligence.
　　REVISED: I have **absolutely** no **illusions** about my **incredible intelligence**.

1. The beautiful foriegn student mistook my complement for an insult, so my first attempt at communication with her was extremely dissappointing.
2. It would be extremely wastful when dineing out too order an outragously priced meal and then eat only half of the food.
3. He is not the heavyest person I know, but he certainly will be paiing for his obesity in later years with wieght-asocciated problems that effect general health.
4. Altogether, the break-ins at the north campus dormatory occured a comparitively few number of times.
5. Term paperes are to be submited with appendixs that thoroghly explain any relevant background information.
6. There are several criterieons that must be met before a student can registar for the senior-level English coarse.
7. Nelson Mandela is truely one the great heros and public speakers of our generation— a man who's speaking voice brings tears to the eyes of some and raises others to action.
8. Like all well-writen Elmore Leonard novels, the plot action builds to a climatic crescendo, and then the author presents an ingenous and unexpectted resolution.
9. In the late 1960s, tie-dying T-shirts and wearing long hare were common phenomenons among young people.
10. The suddeness of Tony's mother's death has left his father in deep confusion and unsure weather burial or cremation would be the best option.
11. Guageing from the few people who attended on this ocassion, Philip is not an extremly popular person on campus.
12. My new girlfriend is a loveable person, posessing great eveness of temperment and even greater keeness of mind.

2.   Spelling, No. 2

If you have problems completing this exercise, review section 14-1 A, B, and C of *Checkmate: A Writing Reference for Canadians, Third Edition.*

This student has not proofread her work. Proofread the essay page and correct all spelling errors.

In Bram Stoker s *Dracula,* their is a complex precence of the foriegn other[1]—those individuales who are not the Western, Christian, white middle- or upper-class male. Dracula, a "monster" and foriegn gentleman who threatens the Western male's identity, is ultimatly destroied despite his brute strength and abundent resourses. Similarlly, the female heroeine, Mina, who uses her "male" skills to lead the British male characters to Dracula, is ultimatly revertted to a domestic position that does not threaten Western patriarchy. The novel's final image of men reassures British male supremacy by glorifing there duty of protectting both women and the English nation as a hole. This problemmatic endding demonstrates that the British male characters must ultimatly displace these "foriegn" powers (good and evil) in order to afirm they're fragile masculine identity, witch is bassed on a patriarchy that must place males above the "foriegn" other. To gain patriarchial "regenerateion"—Anne McClintock notes that Britain mapped its disfunctional concept of patriarchy onto its colonies, therefore reinventting the tradition of the paterfamilias wear the British male was the father figure (McClintock 239-240)— the novel's male characters seak to destroy the foreign male, therebye assertting there masculine identity and British dominence. Also, the novel's heroeine, Mina, is a complex woman who posesses maternal abilitys and "male" skills; the British male characters are unnable to concquer Dracula without her. However, the novel consistenttly demonstrates the male need to control women and too undermine foriegn ability inn order to asert there own mail identity.

_____

[1] In reference to Edward Said's concept of Orientalism, and also in a specifically feminist context, Meyda Yegenoglu demonstrates how "the very desire to penetrate the veiled surface of 'otherness' is constitutive of hegemonic, colonial identity" (Yegenoglu i). She recognizes that "the figure of the Oriental woman has functioned as the veiled interior of Western identity, she calls into question the dualistic conceptions of identity and difference, of East and West" (Yegenoglu i). Hence, any Western portrayal of "otherness" symbolizes not only conditions in the East but also those in the West.

3.   Using Hyphens Correctly

If you have problems completing this exercise, review section 14-2 of *Checkmate: A Writing Reference for Canadians, Third Edition*.

Edit the sentences by supplying needed hyphens or spaces. If a sentence has no errors, write "correct" beside it.

EXAMPLE: On her ultraexpensive ecotour, Jessica was shocked to see a man eating tiger.

REVISED: On her **ultra-expensive** ecotour, Jessica was shocked to see a **man-eating** tiger.

1. Strangely, my half brother has more in common with his stepmother than with his biological father.

2. After carefully weighing the income and daycare options, my brother in law has decided to become a stay at home dad.

3. The eighteen year old gang member was becoming well known to local police.

4. To make a liquor purchase at the duty free shop, one has to be at least nineteen years old.

5. Lenore was able to rent a bed sitting room with a fold out bed in a turn of the century house near the campus.

6. My foster father is poor at decision making and cannot make up his mind whether he wants to rent a one, two, or three bedroom apartment.

7. About one third of the seventy eight elk in the herd had the life threatening illness and had to be destroyed.

8. Ex premier Davis was among the all powerful people at the mid July political fundraiser.

9. The semiinvalid young man painted the most richly detailed and lifelike picture of a Pacific Rim sunset that I have ever seen.

10. Although a selfproclaimed champion of human rights, the president elect has sweeping powers that could make him a quasidictator.

11. Once the upholstery on our old orange sofa started to show its age, we decided to recover it with a neutral coloured fabric. Then, we replaced our halllamp.

12. When the contract of the Raptors' backup centre expired, the team made a strong bid to resign him.

4.   Capitalization

If you have problems completing this exercise, review section 14-3 of *Checkmate: A Writing Reference for Canadians, Third Edition.*

Use proofreaders' marks to correct capitalization errors in the sentences and paragraph below.

EXAMPLE: President John. f. Kennedy did not like Canadian prime minister John Diefenbaker.

REVISED: Correct, using proofreader's marks, to read: President John. F. Kennedy did not like Prime Minister John Diefenbaker.

1. what a pity that bern, switzerland, dropped out of the competition for the upcoming winter olympics.

2. Our Christmas french examination will be held on Tuesday, December 20, at 3:30 p.m.

3. My Uncle always complains that fireworks on Canada day are a waste of time and money.

4. Last saturday, Don Cherry had an interview with the great one during his "coach's corner" segment on cbc's *Hockey night in Canada.*

5. Each time Damon visited his doctor on Danforth avenue in Toronto, he made a point of stopping at the Athenian Garden restaurant for a feed of greek food.

6. The Acting Mayor visited an Exhibition of modernist painting at the Vancouver art gallery.

7. A valuable information source for any essay on The History of Women's Sports in Canada is *the Canadian encyclopedia.* Here, one can learn about the great women's basketball team the Edmonton grads, more formally known as the Commercial Graduates basketball club. During the period from 1915 to 1940, the grads sported an incredible 93 percent victory record. In 1924, the team played 6 games in conjunction with women's olympics held in paris. In 1926, the Grads won the french and european Championships and later played 9 games in conjunction with the 1936 Berlin olympics. dr. james Naismith, the canadian-born inventor of basketball, once said, "the Grads are the finest basketball team that ever stepped out on a floor."

5.   Using Abbreviations Correctly

If you have problems completing this exercise, review section 14-4 of *Checkmate: A Writing Reference for Canadians, Third Edition*.

Edit the sentences to correct any abbreviation errors. If a sentence has no errors, write "correct" beside it.

EXAMPLE: Dr. Sue Allison will teach at SFU near Van. until Xmas.

REVISED: Dr. **Susan** Allison will teach at **Simon Fraser University** near **Vancouver** until **Christmas**.

1. After Madeline Deter completed her MBA. at Harvard U., she was appointed CFO at CTV.

2. Dr. Wil. C. Gibson PhD, Chancellor of the U., will welcome graduates and their guests to the convocation.

3. The Anthro. 321 prof. told her students that the first specimens of Java Man were found in 1891 A.D and 1892 C.E.

4. My dr. prescribed some antibiotics for my severe cold, and I took the first dosage in the p.m. when I got home.

5. Our theatre reservations are for 4:30 pm and the cost of each ticket is $89. dollars for a balcony seat.

6. The heavyweight championship fight was held c. 1918 and featured Joe "Sweat Glands" Palooka vs. S. "Bonecrusher" Smith.

7. The PM's plane will land at J.F.K. Airport in N.Y., N.Y., in the a.m.; in the afternoon, he will give a speech to the UN Security Council, and in the evening he will attend a dinner hosted by Canada's representative at the UN, Guillermo Rishchynski.

8. The publication is being produced jointly by the Department of Indian & Northern Affairs and the Department of Consumer & Corporate Affairs.

9. When he arrived at the unemployment office, he discovered he did not have a record of his SIN number.

10. The firm of Wyecroft, Trafalgar & Simpson will handle the litigation on the Jones case.

11. In the botany experiment, we observed that the plant had grown twenty-three cm over the two-week period.

6. Using Numbers Correctly

If you have problems completing this exercise, review section 14-5 of *Checkmate: A Writing Reference for Canadians, Third Edition.*

Edit the sentence to correct any errors with the use of numbers. If a sentence has no errors, write "correct" beside it.

EXAMPLE: The paid attendance was 19 800, but only fifteen thousand actually attended the basketball game.

REVISED: The paid attendance was 19 800, but only 15 000 actually attended the basketball game.

1. 32 people were killed in the sinking of a Greek ferry last September.
2. For the August fifteenth performance of Shakespeare in the Park, there was a paid attendance of one hundred and seventy-eight, so the total profit was four thousand, eight hundred and ninety-five dollars.
3. Mackenzie King's greatest legislative achievement was the Industrial Disputes Investigation Act of 1907, but he is perhaps best remembered for introducing conscription for the defence of Canada in nineteen forty.
4. Act Five, Scene Three in *Taming of the Shrew* opens with Bianca saying, "Good sister, wrong me not nor wrong yourself."
5. On September thirtieth, 2002, the federal government announced an environmental policy that would call for the banning of truck traffic on the four hundred and one highway.
6. Page 9 was the end of the fax transmission; there was no page 10.
7. The invitation states that the book launch will be held at seventeen Government St., commencing at 8 o'clock in the evening.
8. Only 75 percent of the 130 000 Grade 10 Ontario secondary school students who took the literacy examination passed.
9. Ottawa is host to one of the world's largest resident diplomatic corps: one hundred and five embassies and high commissions, of which seventy-three are from developing countries.
10. From 1963 to 1973, the Soviets won eleven of twelve Olympic and world championships; in 1972, Canada managed to win the Canada-Soviet hockey series with a record of four victories, three losses, and one tie.
11. The fifteen m Canadarm functions like a human arm and has six joints: two at its shoulder, one at its elbow, and three at its wrist.
12. Of the twenty-one million people in the small Eastern European country, only 275 000 voted for the leftist candidate.

7. *Italics* and <u>Underlining</u>

If you have problems completing this exercise, review section 14-6 of *Checkmate: A Writing Reference for Canadians, Third Edition*.

Edit the sentences below to correct any errors in the use of italics or underlining. If a sentence has no errors, write "correct" beside it.

> EXAMPLE: The Victoria Colonist reports that the mayor will head an *ad hoc* committee.
> REVISED: *The Victoria Colonist* reports that the mayor will head an ad hoc committee.

1. Teresa Sandhu will give a short oral presentation based on her M.A. thesis, *Social distance and the pidginized speech of Punjabi women in British Columbia*.
2. In "Calvin and Hobbes," Waterson often makes a wry comment on the human condition through the voices of his cartoon characters.
3. It is unfair to compare Morley Callaghan's short story *A Cap for Steve* with his longer works such as the novel "A Fine and Private Balance."
4. Fans of CBC's Hockey Night in Canada were chagrined to learn of Ron MacLean's possible departure as host of the popular sports show.
5. Gordon Lightfoot's affecting song The Wreck of the Edmund Fitzgerald tells about the sinking of the "Edmund Fitzgerald" in *Lake Erie*.
6. The student cinema will hold an Orson Welles film festival featuring, of course, *Citizen Kane* (1941), as well as Welles' lesser-known works, such as *The Magnificent Ambersons* (1942), *The Lady from Shanghai* (1948), and *Touch of Evil* (1958).
7. The painting "Church and Horse," 1974, by Canada's Alex Colville perfectly complements Alice Munro's classic short story *Boys and Girls* in the *anthology*.
8. At a vertically challenged four feet and five inches in height, Calvin suffers from a folie de grandeur if he thinks he can become a starting centre in the NBA.
9. When I was dealt a 7 at *Casinorama*, Delores called me lucky, but her definition of lucky and mine are at odds since I lost $10 000.
10. The "*Globe and Mail*" has a regular feature called *Facts & Arguments*, which I often find enlightening or amusing.
11. My neighbour strongly indicated that he would not call the police *again*.
12. The author of the article in *Maclean's* suggests that the South American general's *aide-de-camp* was a conspirator.

8.   Spelling and Mechanics Review

If you have problems completing this exercise, review chapter 14 of *Checkmate: A Writing Reference for Canadians, Third Edition.*

Edit the résumé to correct any problems with spelling or mechanics.

Natalie singh
1412 Prince Dr.
Markham, Ontar.
M3H 2L4
(nine zero five) 945-3876
electronic-mail: nsingh@presto.com

OBJECTIVE: to become an investigative journallist specializzing in educational isues.

SKILLS
_   Abillity to research thoroghly and meticulouslly useing a wide range of traditional and new mediums.
_   Proficientcy in analyzing information and statistical datas.
_   *Excellent* writing and editorrial skills.
_   Strong project managment skills; able to complete complex assignments on time.
_   Highly computer-literate having mastered many wordprocessing, graphics, and desk-top design programs.

_

WORK EXPERIENCE
Research Intern. U. of Waterloo. April-Sept. 2001–2003. Asssisted in educational research projects for 3 professors.
Administrative Assistant Intern. B.C. Min. of Education. April-September 2000–2001. Helped administer and improve a computer records filing system in the Assessment Branch.
Market Research. Ed lottenville group. March–October 1999. Conducted telephone research to determine needs of decision-maker in the tele-communications industry.

ADDITIONAL EXPERIENCE
Adult Literacy volunteer tutor. taught basic literacy skills to young adults who had severe developmental problems.

EDUCATION
Carelton University, Ottawa, Ontario. Bachelor of A. (Journal.) expected in 2004. Activities: Ocean kayaking, Reading, Yoga

PUBLICATIONS
Circular Home. "The Gainville Star," December fifteenth, 1999, p. E2.
"Insulating Your Basement." Canadian Home Life, Spring 1998, p. 52

References availible upon request.

Chapter 15: *ELL (English Language Learners)*

1.   Articles

If you have problems completing this exercise, review section 15-1 of *Checkmate: A Writing Reference for Canadians, Third Edition.*

Underline the correct article or articles in each sentence or pair of sentences. If no article is needed, cross out the parenthesized articles.

1. He was (a, an, the) unlikely candidate for the election.

2. There was a gorgeous sports car in the display window. (A, An, The) car was black.

3. Jason wore a powder-blue shirt on his first day of work. It was (a, an, the) permanent-press shirt.

4. After trying to lift the enormous rock without bending his knees, he needed (a, an, the) hernia operation.

5. Sometimes it is difficult being (a, an, the) only child.

6. (A, An, The) book you requested last Wednesday is now available at (a, an, the) special orders desk.

7. If college does not work out, you could always enlist in (a, an, the) armed services.

8. Cyril invited me over to play (a, an, the) game of chess.

9. The cover of Erika Ritter's new book says that it was shortlisted for (a, an, the) Writers' Trust Non-Fiction Prize.

10. If you believe (a, an, the) latest issue of *New Brunswick Business*, there is not (a, an, the) richer man in (a, an, the) province.

11. For recreation she plays (a, an, the) little hockey on (a, an, the) weekend.

12. (A, An, the) snakes are reptiles.

2. Editing for Correct Articles

If you have problems completing this exercise, review section 15-1 of *Checkmate: A Writing Reference for Canadians, Third Edition.*

Articles have been omitted from the passage below. Edit the paragraphs so articles are used correctly. In a few instances, alternatives are acceptable.

EXAMPLE: Architect Douglas Cardinal was born in Calgary but grew up on farm outside Red Deer.

REVISED: Architect Douglas Cardinal was born in Calgary but grew up on **a** farm outside Red Deer.

Architect Douglas Cardinal was born in Calgary, but grew up on farm outside Red Deer, Alberta. His mother predicted he would be architect—even as young boy he loved to construct things with building blocks. His father was game warden whose deep love of nature was part of his Blackfoot heritage. He showed his son beauty of land and taught him about ways in which nature solves many problems.

Douglas Cardinal studied architecture at University of British Columbia and University of Texas. He opened architectural office in Edmonton in 1967 and produced varied but innovative body of work. He has designed Edmonton Space Sciences Centre, schools, churches, homes, and many other buildings. His buildings are unique because of their curving shapes, which resemble Canadian landscape.

Douglas Cardinal's architectural firm was one of first to use computer-aided drafting system (CAD). Arguably his greatest design accomplishment is Museum of Civilization in Hull, Quebec. This building plays key role in our nation's cultural life, housing artifacts that help Canadians learn about their past. For example, museum features great hall filled with totem poles.

Without doubt, Cardinal is one of most famous architects in Canada, and supremely gifted artist.

3. Helping Verbs and Main Verbs

If you have problems completing this exercise, review section 15-2 A and B of *Checkmate: A Writing Reference for Canadians, Third Edition.*

Edit the sentences to correct any problem with main verbs or helping verbs. If a sentence has no errors, write "correct" beside it.

EXAMPLE: Deidre have been an employee for ten years before she resigned last May.

REVISED: Deidre ~~have~~ **had** been an employee for ten years before she resigned last May.

1. The town councillors has asked the person applying for regional manager to be at the meeting this Tuesday.

2. We was planning a trip to Fredericton next summer.

3. I will have did all the assigned questions for geometry by the course deadline.

4. Today, my three-year-old nephew have eaten five helpings of spaghetti at one sitting.

5. My landlady is been a pain in the neck.

6. Arnold's father will been going to the same mechanic for ten years now.

7. I will be talking with my aunt for about five minutes when she telephones later today.

8. I is working on the term essay that counts for fifty percent of our final mark.

9. Canadian television audiences will had been watching CBC programs for sixty years in 2012.

10. My parents are intend to take a trip to Greece when they retire.

11. In some commentators' eyes, Obama and Putin are been hailed as champions of the war against terrorism.

12. You ever see anything so incredible at a hockey game before?

13. Miles complained that we never taken his contributions seriously during the entire term.

14. I feel confident that you will get an interview for the job.

15. The dunce will has been standing in the corner for five hours in about two minutes.

4. Editing Helping Verbs and Main Verbs

If you have problems completing this exercise, review section 15-2 A and B of *Checkmate: A Writing Reference for Canadians, Third Edition*.

The following passage has many verb errors. Edit it to correct any errors with helping *and* main verbs.

EXAMPLE: I must has been about ten at the time.

REVISED: I must **have** been about ten at the time.

I will always remember my first trip through the Rockies. I must has been about ten at the time. As I recall, my mother have been planning the trip for about a year. My father were continually taking summer courses at university, so the trip gave him time to be alone and concentrate on his studies.

We boarded the train in Vancouver late at night and, as always, my sister were cranky because she don't get enough sleep. Soon, the train were pulling out of the Vancouver train station and our long-awaited journey have finally begun.

We has been travelling on large boats for years, but travelling on a train were a completely new experience to my sister and me. Naturally, as kids, we has to explore every nook and cranny of the train. Most of our time were spent in the glass-domed observation car, watching day and night as the British Columbia landscape went pass by.

Eventually we approached the Rockies. Until then I have never seen anything so wondrous in my young life. It was absolutely stunning!

Now that I am in my early twenties, I often look back at the incredible trip and wonder if I will ever has such an overwhelming experience again. I'm sure that I will never had a vacation like that again.

You ever has a childhood experience like that?

5.   **Helping Verbs: Modal Verbs**

If you have problems completing this exercise, review Section 15-2 A of *Checkmate: A Writing Reference for Canadians, Third Edition.*

Edit the sentences to correct problems with modal helping verbs, other helping verbs, or main verbs. If there are no errors in a sentence, write "correct."

EXAMPLE: My uncle can bench-press his own weight when he was my age.

EXAMPLE: My uncle ~~can~~could bench-press his own weight when he was my age.

1. He can have returned the library book yesterday without a fine; however, today he could not do that.

2. I will had to buy more bulk paper if I want to print out a complete copy of the essay tomorrow.

3. I may inform you that your interesting short story "My Life as an Over-ripe Tomato" does not meet our publishing needs at the present time.

4. You would take a glove to the baseball game just in case a foul ball is hit in your direction.

5. Darcy should have took a glove to last Friday's baseball game since a foul ball landed right in front of her.

6. Thomas use to worry about final exams; however, now he meditates and takes yoga and doesn't worry as much anymore.

7. The family will rather visit St. John's in the summer than during a severe winter blizzard.

8. The weather person on the television says chances are good that it can rain tomorrow.

9. Marcie can have been accepted into the prestigious computer science program if her mark in calculus had been one letter grade higher.

10. We could have another Walkerton on our hands if something isn't quickly done to improve drinking water inspection programs across Canada.

11. Jeff has better listen to the coach's warning or he would be thrown off the varsity team.

12. I shall have left my bank card in the ATM.

Chapter 15: ELL

6. Verbs Followed by Gerunds or Infinitives

If you have problems completing this exercise, review section 15-2 G of *Checkmate: A Writing Reference for Canadians, Third Edition*.

For each sentence underline whether a gerund, an infinitive, or both should or could be used. In some instances, an unmarked infinitive (without "to") may be acceptable.

EXAMPLE: The school principal will not tolerate .

(<u>bullying</u>, to bully)

1. I would hate ____ the opportunity for the job.

   (losing, to lose)

2. He remembered ____ his keys on the night stand by the window.

   (placing, to place)

3. Jennifer was homesick for Kamloops and missed ____ walks along the Thompson River.

   (taking, to take)

4. Mr. Sanji quit ____ squash after he tore some knee cartilage and needed surgery.

   (playing, to play)

5. Everyone on our floor in the residence volunteered ____ groceries at the food bank.

   (packing, to pack)

6. Thankfully, my uncle persuaded me ____ all my high-technology stocks.

   (selling, to sell)

7. Everything has been tabulated, and now I would like ____ the winner of the frosh week worm-eating contest.

   (announcing, to announce)

8. I would like Gretchen ____ with me about claiming her grand prize.

   (meeting, to meet)

9. Be quiet and listen to the creek ____.

   (babble, babbling, to babble)

10. Help the lady with two broken arms ____ the heavy door.

   (open, to open, opening)

11. Due to illness, the award-winning author postponed ____ to Saskatoon.

   (coming, to come)

7.   More Practice with Verbs Followed by Gerunds and Infinitives

If you have problems completing this exercise, review section 15-2 G of *Checkmate: A Writing Reference for Canadians, Third Edition*.

In the passage below, base verbs are provided beneath the blanks. Decide whether a gerund or an infinitive follows the verb. (Note: In some cases, an unmarked infinitive—that is, without *to*—may be acceptable.)

  EXAMPLE: George Chuvalo started <u>to box</u> at an early age.

(box)

George Chuvalo started ___ at an early age. He decided ___ professional box at

(box)   (turn)

the age of 19 and won the Canadian Heavyweight Championship in 1956. His victory

was claimed ___ James J. Park. Many boxing fans remember Chuvalo ___ toe-to-

(defeat)   (stand)

toe with the great Muhammad Ali and ___ brutal blows. Numerous boxing

(exchange)

commentators acknowledge Chuvalo as ___ the greatest, or at least toughest,

(be)

Canadian heavyweight boxer ever. He always knew his limitations and strengths, and he never

pretended ___a finesse boxer. Rather, he challenged himself ___ the best he

(be)   (be)

could be with the skills he had. Chuvalo expected ___ whenever he entered the ring,

(win)

and that confidence always showed in his determined performances.

  Since he quit boxing ___ other areas of interest, Chuvalo has been a much

(pursue)

sought-after speaker at Canadian high schools. Through his speeches, he helps students ___ the ravages of drug use.

(avoid)

8.   Phrasal Verbs

If you have problems completing this exercise, review section 15-2 H of *Checkmate: A Writing Reference for Canadians, Third Edition*.

Edit the sentences to correct any errors with phrasal verbs. In some instances, there is more than one correct possibility. If so, give both. If the sentence has no error, write "correct" below it.

EXAMPLE: Jesse will the new skates try on.

REVISED: Jesse will try the new skates on. / Jesse will try on the new skates.

1. I threw the dog food that Ace hadn't bothered to touch out.

   _____

2. James will ask out the girl he met at the floor party last Wednesday night.

   _____

3. Jack, Ali, and Jon met for a few hours to go their group report over before they presented it to the class.

   _____

4. After she had her operation, Nelson looked his grandmother after for a few days.

   _____

5. I plan to make the weekly test up at a later date.

   _____

6. The clerk in the administration offices handed me another form and told me to fill out it.

   _____

7. Because of inclement weather, race organizers decided to call the race in benefit of the hospital and various children's charities off.

   _____

8. I understood the answer after Marcel broke the calculus question down.

   _____

9. After the hot summer we had, many people will look installing pools into.

   _____

10. Once the party is over, a crew the mess will clean up.

   _____

9.   Using Appropriate Verb Tenses in Conditional Sentences

If you have problems completing this exercise, review section 15-2 J of *Checkmate: A Writing Reference for Canadians, Third Edition.*

Give the correct verb tenses in the blanks. You may need to provide helping verbs, including modals.

EXAMPLE: Whenever Julie ate her mom's XXX chili, she <u>got</u> heartburn.

(get)

1. When a solar eclipse occurs, the moon ___ out the sun.

(block)

2. You ___ the jackpot if three aces appear on the slot machine.

(win)

3. Whenever Selma prepared her notorious undercooked chicken, her dinner guests all ___ sick.

(get)

4. If I don't get the position I want with IBM, I ___ to another corporation.

(apply)

5. If they had a place in the country, they ___ horses.

(keep)

6. If you try to play squash without properly warming up, you ___ a muscle.

(pull)

7. You ___ a passing mark if you study the material we covered in class.

(receive)

8. The children ___ colds if they go outside without their coats.

(catch)

9. If I had ignored the financial advisors at my local bank, I ___ more money in my portfolio today.

(have)

10.   Editing for Appropriate Verb Tenses in Conditional Sentences

If you have problems completing this exercise, review section 15-2 J of *Checkmate: A Writing Reference for Canadians, Third Edition*.

In the passage below, provide the correct verb tense including, if necessary, helping verbs.

EXAMPLE: The International Space Station <u>will represent</u> a move of
(represent)
unprecedented scale.

It seems that whenever humans invest in space exploration, the spin-offs in terms
of scientific knowledge and technological development ___ amazing. If scientists
(be)
and planners are correct in their predictions, this ___ true of the International Space
(be)
Station. In fact, some medical researchers think we ___ new drugs for the
(develop)
treatment and possibly a cure for cancer if medical research conducted in space-station
laboratories proves as fruitful as expected.

Here is just one exciting medical area where space-station research could lead us. More pure
protein crystals may be grown in space than on Earth. Analysis of these crystals helps scientists
better understand the nature of proteins, enzymes, and viruses. If scientists better understand
these fundamental building blocks of life, perhaps they ___ able to develop new drugs. If this
(be)
research progresses as scientists think it will, it

___ to the study of possible treatments for cancer, diabetes, emphysema, and
(lead)
immune system disorders.

Many people question the amount of money spent on space exploration and
research, but if it is not, these exciting possibilities for medical advancement ___
(be)
delayed or even lost. In fact, if we had only invested more money
earlier, medical science ___ further along today.
(be)

11. Using Correct Verb Tenses with Indirect Quotations

If you have problems completing this exercise, review section 15-2 K of *Checkmate: A Writing Reference for Canadians, Third Edition*.

Circle the letter of the option that is the correct indirect quotation of each original quotation.

1. "It may be those who do most, dream most."
   —Stephen Leacock
   a) Stephen Leacock says it may be those who do most, dream most.
   b) Stephen Leacock says it may be those who did most, dreamt most.
   c) Stephen Leacock says it may be those who will do most, will dream most.

2. "I don't care what is written about me so long as it isn't true."
   —Katharine Hepburn
   a) Katharine Hepburn said she don't care what is written about me so long as it isn't true.
   b) Katharine Hepburn said that she didn't care what was written about her so long as it wasn't true.
   c) Katharine Hepburn said she doesn't care what is written about me so long as it wasn't true.

3. "Advertising is legalized lying."
   —H.G. Wells
   a) H.G. Wells said that advertising was legalized lying.
   b) H.G. Wells says that advertising was legalized lying.
   c) H.G. Wells said that advertising is legalized lying.

4. "I was a freethinker before I knew how to think."
   —George Bernard Shaw
   a) George Bernard Shaw said I was a freethinker before I knew how to think.
   b) George Bernard Shaw said that he was a freethinker before he knew how to think.
   c) George Bernard Shaw says that he was a freethinker before he knew how to think.

5. "We live in a world ruined by Reason."
   —David Mamet
   a) David Mamet says they lived in a world ruined by Reason.
   b) David Mamet says that we live in a world ruined by Reason.
   c) David Mamet says that we lived in a world ruined by Reason.

12. Words You Can Omit and Those You Cannot

If you have problems completing this exercise, review section 15-3 A and B of *Checkmate: A Writing Reference for Canadians, Third Edition.*

In the sentences below, add words that are needed and delete words that are not.

EXAMPLE: The resort town where she lives there, it get busy during the summer vacation.

REVISED: The resort town where she lives **can** get busy during the summer vacation.

1. The British Columbia coast line very irregular.

2. Round homes do not have the surface area of conventional homes; therefore, lose less heat.

3. Are countless sound reasons for reducing greenhouse gas emissions.

4. As you will note from my comments at the end of your essay, is clear that you must closely check your final essay copy for grammar and spelling errors.

5. Is a long way to Tipperary.

6. The biology teaching assistant he helped me understand how osmosis contributes to kidney function.

7. The package Aunt Lil sent it contained her inedible fruit cake as a Christmas gift.

8. Wanda often parks in the spot that I want to park in it.

9. The college where she is enrolled there has an award-winning design program.

10. The sports car it can reach amazing speeds in mere seconds.

11. At the press conference, the Olympic athlete said are many reasons for her early retirement from the sport.

12. Late at night, can be quite dangerous to walk alone in that part of the city.

13.   Placement of Adjectives and Adverbs

If you have problems completing this exercise, review section 15-3 C, D, and E of *Checkmate: A Writing Reference for Canadians, Third Edition.*

Place adjectives in the correct order and adverbs in the correct position within each sentence. If the sentence has no order or placement problems, write "correct" beside it.

EXAMPLE: In the wok second she placed the green, fresh, chopped onions.

REVISED: Second, she placed the fresh, chopped, green onions in the wok.

1. A red Chinese oblong box arrived yesterday only.

2. The Mexican gold modern bracelet dangled from her loosely wrist.

3. The first ancient Muslim vase was transported quickly to the Vancouver museum.

4. Charles Lindbergh crossed successfully seemingly endless the grey Atlantic Ocean.

5. I looked for then a silk lime-green narrow tie to go with my corduroy blue tapered shirt.

6. In the garage, Gavin tripped over the green tiny first garden gnome.

7. Stephen has managed to complete the backward new daring dive occasionally.

8. The illuminating ancient Jewish proverb was prominently displayed on the notice board.

9. Rather is Jason quiet around an older large imposing crowd.

10. The stuntwoman's fall was broken fortunately by the soft rectangular large mattress.

11. Gordon's Lightfoot's best beautiful early songs are frequently ballads.

12. On the table delicately Kati placed the porcelain German two figurines.

14.   Present and Past Participles as Adjectives

If you have problems completing this exercise, review section 15-3 F of *Checkmate: A Writing Reference for Canadians, Third Edition*.

Write the correct adjective participle, present or past, in the spaces provided.

EXAMPLE: I was <u>amazed</u> by the <u>pleasing</u> portrait the three-year-old

(amazing, amazed)   (pleasing, pleased)

artist created.

1. Tim made a very ___ remark about Adul's weight, and I was most

(insulting, insulted)

___ by the tone he used to make the comment.

(insulting, insulted)

2. The novel *The Corrections* was a very ___ read.

(satisfying, satisfied)

3. Wheat is surely one of the most important crops ___ in

(producing, produce)

Saskatchewan.

4. My eighty-five-year-old aunt had a ___ return flight to Vancouver.

(tiring, tired)

5. After studying for three consecutive nights without any sleep, Quan had a very ___ look on his face.

(tiring, tired)

6. For Dustin, it was an ___ task to learn to speak a foreign

(overwhelming, overwhelmed)

language fluently.

7. The documentary offered a ___ look at polar ice caps.

(fascinating, fascinated)

8. Most urban drivers display an ___ lack of courtesy towards fellow

motorists.   (appalled, appalling)

9. The doctor is very ___ in stem-cell research.

(interesting, interested)

15. Correctly Using Prepositions to Show Time and Place

If you have problems completing this exercise, review section 15-3 G of *Checkmate: A Writing Reference for Canadians, Third Edition*.

Part 1: Edit each sentence so that all prepositions are correct. If a sentence has no errors, write "correct" beside it.

  EXAMPLE: In July 17, the mail carrier left a small package for me on the mailbox.

  REVISED: **On** July 17, the mail carrier left a small package for me **in** the mailbox.

a. We plan to hold the meeting on two weeks at the floor lounge.

b. I have been at Moose Jaw before, but not in this time of the year.

c. The memorial service for veterans will be held on Monday, November 11, at 11 a.m.

d. At breakfast, he read about the Raptors' overtime win in the newspaper.

e. In night, it is difficult to read street numbers at the front of a house.

f. In the daytime, she found it difficult to sleep in a plane.

g. She aimed her last shot on the 8-ball.

Part 2: Edit the wedding invitation to correct all preposition problems.

Your are cordially invited to the marriage of

Jillian Wendy Solnicki

and

Russel Wing Singh

in Saturday, June 7, 2004

on 11 o'clock at the morning

in St. Bart's Ukrainian Church

at the town of Alton, Ontario.

Reception will follow

on the Kon-Tiki Room

of the Alton Inn.

Glossary of Usage

1.   Using Words Correctly

If you have problems completing this exercise, review pages 561-580 of *Checkmate: A Writing Reference for Canadians, Third Edition*.

Edit each sentence below by correcting any misused words.

EXAMPLE: Forced out of the company for which he had worked for thirty-five years, the engineer could not except his fate.

REVISED: Forced out of the company for which he had worked for thirty-five years, the engineer could not except **accept** his fate.

1. Despite his strong convictions, Jacquim is not adverse to having a drink of good wine on special occasions.

2. After years of diligent practice, the swimmer is already for the Olympic trials.

3. The prime minister eluded to his chief rival when he mentioned the short-lived popularity of former Prime Minister Kim Campbell.

4. The choice of starting point guard for the junior varsity basketball team is among Stephanie and Clarissa.

5. It requires a certain set of climactic conditions for a hurricane to occur.

6. Sandra was extremely discrete for not divulging her roommate's numerous psychological problems.

7. The master of ceremonies gave a glowing introduction to the visiting professor that was highly appropriate for such an imminent guest.

8. The agent had trouble selling the house after prospective buyers found out there had been an elicit hydroponic garden in the basement.

9. Uncle Nick advised me to precede with caution when exploring old mine shafts.

10. Its my favourite quote from T.S. Eliot's *The Wasteland*.

11. At the club, Margaret spent hours and hours riding the stationery bicycle.

12. If you are not sure of the name of the person who holds the position when you write the letter, address it "TO WHO IT MAY CONCERN."

Chapter 9: GRAMMAR

1.   Identify and Classify Nouns

1. <u>Patrice</u> will visit <u>Calgary</u> in <u>December</u> with her <u>family</u>.

    1   1   1   5

2. The <u>theme</u> of the <u>haiku poem</u> was the <u>essence</u> of <u>love</u>.

        4   2   4   4

3. <u>Rain</u> fell in <u>Ucluelet</u>, <u>British Columbia</u>, for five long <u>days</u>.

     6   1   1   7

4. The great <u>writer Vladimir Nabokov</u> held the <u>butterfly</u> in

             2   1   3

his outstretched <u>hand</u>.

                 3

5. <u>Rocky's touchdown pass</u> in the dying <u>seconds</u> of the <u>game</u>

         8   7   2

was a <u>thing</u> of <u>beauty</u>.

    2   4

6. <u>Sir John A. Macdonald</u> led <u>Canada</u> to <u>unity</u>.

      1   1   4

7. According to <u>Richard J. Needham</u>, <u>people</u> "won't steal <u>anything</u> that is red-hot or

             1   2   2

embedded in <u>concrete</u>."

           3

8. The <u>sun's rays</u> warmed us and gentle <u>breezes</u> caressed the <u>desert sands</u>.

        8   2   3

9. <u>Hail</u> wrought <u>destruction</u> on the <u>crops</u> in south central <u>Saskatchewan</u>.

   6   4   2   1

10. <u>Cities</u> are good <u>places</u> in which to appreciate <u>culture</u>.

     2   2   4

2.   Pronouns

1. The Sindarthas are coming to <u>our</u> home at 4 p.m., and I expect **<u>they</u>** will stay for dinner.

2. I hope <u>you</u> will join Dwayne and **<u>me</u>** for the evening news.

3. When Gillian took **<u>her</u>** shopping, <u>she</u> parked <u>her</u> car by the police station and returned to find that <u>it</u> had been stolen.

4. The money <u>my</u> rich uncle left to <u>me</u> is **<u>mine</u>** to do with as <u>I</u> wish; <u>my</u> brothers and sisters can spend **<u>theirs</u>** as <u>they</u> please.

5. Drivers **<u>who</u>** travel in the passing lane should always keep to the posted speed limit.

6. **<u>That</u>** archer will probably make <u>our</u> next Olympic team if <u>she</u> continues <u>her</u> phenomenal progress.

7. **<u>Whose</u>** minivan are <u>we</u> taking to <u>my</u> graduation?

8. <u>She</u> carries **<u>herself</u>** very well and plans to be the world's next wealthy supermodel.

9. Since Marion and <u>I</u> live only a block apart, <u>we</u> frequently visit **<u>one another</u>**.

10. **<u>Everyone</u>** wanted to come to <u>my</u> 1980s nostalgia party.

3.   Verbs (Answers)

1. The starter <u>fired</u> the gun.

2. Tornadoes occasionally <u>occur</u> in south central Ontario.

3. My father <u>has been</u> a widower for six years.

4. Margaret <u>detests</u> elevators.

5. The wet dog <u>shook</u>.

6. I <u>feel</u> anxious about the final chemistry examination.

7. She <u>had wanted</u> to be a lumberjack since her early childhood.

8. You <u>should have written</u> to me before arriving at my doorstep for a six-week holiday.

9. They <u>take</u> singing lessons with my brother-in-law.

10. We <u>will be</u> <u>visiting</u> all the castles in an eastern region of Portugal during our trip.

11. Colm <u>had painted</u> the ceiling with an oil-based paint.

12. He <u>approached</u> every essay assignment with an open mind.

13. <u>Don't give</u> me any back talk!

14. If I <u>were</u> wealthier, I <u>would travel</u> more.

15. The convicted prisoner <u>was taken</u> to the execution room.

4. Adjectives, Articles, and Adverbs

1. The old mattress is very comfortable.

   D

2. Her novel echoes a story from classical literature.

                   I

3. Ali enthusiastically approached the learning task with childlike curiosity.

                         D

4. It is wishful thinking to completely base your retirement plans on the hope that

                                                              D

   you will win a provincial lottery.

           I

5. A victimless crime is still an unacceptable act.

   I   I

6. The elderly master of ceremonies read the winners' names slowly but clearly.

   D

7. Climate change is an extremely important environmental problem.

                       I

8. Giovanni plays the classical guitar really well.

                   D

9. Fortunately, when the accident-prone stuntman fell out of the helicopter, there

                   D

   was a soft haystack below him.

       I

10. The Korean exchange student can run faster than anyone I know, but she is

    D

   certainly not the fastest sprinter on campus.

                   D

5.   Prepositions, Conjunctions, and Interjections

1. Allanna is not associated <u>with</u> the group that wrote graffiti <u>on</u> washroom walls <u>or</u> the mob that overturned the statue <u>of</u> the university president.

2. Yes, I will return the book <u>to</u> the library <u>and</u> pay the accumulated fine.

3. You can slip the completed essay <u>under</u> the professor's office door <u>or</u> ask a secretary to place it <u>in</u> the mailbox.

4. Melody's room is <u>opposite</u> mine <u>in</u> the residence, <u>yet</u> she studies so hard <u>that</u> I have not seen her <u>in</u> ages.

5. I am not registering <u>for</u> the intramural hockey league this year, <u>so</u> there is no point buying new equipment.

6. <u>Neither</u> sleet <u>nor</u> snow will keep mail carriers <u>or</u> plumbers <u>from</u> finding their way <u>to</u> our door.

7. No, you cannot drive a motorcycle <u>without</u> a helmet <u>and</u> a valid driver's license.

8. It is wise to live <u>within</u> your means; <u>however</u>, you have to spend money to make money.

9. <u>Not only</u> Carol Shields <u>but also</u> Rohinton Mistry was nominated <u>for</u> the prestigious literary award.

10. Ouch, it hurt <u>when</u> I was struck <u>by</u> lightning <u>on</u> the shoulder <u>and</u> <u>under</u> the arm.

6.   Sentence Subjects

1. The <u>challenging and breathtaking highway</u> snakes through the Alberni Valley to Tofino.

2. The <u>mild climate</u> of Victoria, British Columbia, attracts many university students and retirees.

3. <u>Margaret Atwood and Mordecai Richler</u> are famous Canadian novelists.

4. Red and black <u>poppies</u> appear on lapels across the nation during November.

5. For a time, <u>Vancouver</u>, British Columbia, and <u>Lucerne</u>, <u>Switzerland</u>, were in contention for the Winter Olympics.

6. [<u>You</u>] Act now or not at all.

7. There is a <u>distinct possibility</u> that a <u>special guest</u> will attend the convocation ceremony.

8. There were <u>two security guards</u> in the large crowd.

9. Does <u>Gillian</u> think <u>she</u> will get away with the deception?

11. After considerable debate, the <u>championship game</u> will be on Friday.

7.   Sentence Objects and Complements

1. [Adolescence] [is] [not a bed of roses].

      S   V   SC

2. [The foul ball] [hit] [the first base umpire].

      S   V   DO

3. [The young author] [published] [her second collection of poems].

       S   V   DO

4. [A second collection of poems] [was published] by [the young author].

         S   V   DO

5. [Who] [sold] [you] [that incredible new Bruce Springsteen CD]?

    S   V   IO   DO

6. [The student] [called] [his drama instructor] [a fruit cake].

      S   V   DO   OC

7. [The basketball team] [wins].

       S   V

8. [You] [give] [me] [a five-dollar bill], and [I] [will give] [you] [five loonies].

  S   V IO   DO   S   V   IO   DO

9. [The captain of the debating team] [was] [a senior].

         S   V   SC

10. [Several souvenirs] [were bought] by [our friends].

      S   V   DO

8.   Prepositional Phrases

1. The film on Canada' contribution to World War I is very graphic.

                 adjective

2. The Pattersons ate dinner before driving to the cottage.

                 adverb

3. The hockey team travelled to Lethbridge.

                 Adverb

4. The show dogs <u>in the judging ring</u> are absolutely stunning.

adjective

5. Fydor Dostoevsky wrote *Crime and Punishment* <u>in 1866</u>.

adverb

6. Dale purchased a new car <u>with bucket seats</u>.

adjective

7. The squirrel scurries <u>across the top</u> <u>of our backyard fence</u>.

adverb   adjective

8. You can identify a cardinal <u>by its unique colouring</u>.

adverb

10. The Museum of Civilization <u>in Ottawa</u> was designed <u>by Douglas Cardinal</u>.

adjective   adverb

11. The professors met <u>in private</u> to discuss the English courses <u>for next year</u>.

adverb   adjective

9.   Verbal Phrases:

1. The rabbit, <u>bounding and dodging</u>, crossed Lucy's path.

Present participial phrase; functions as an adjective modifying *rabbit*.

2. <u>Standing</u> is not good for your circulation.

   Gerund phrase; functions as a noun and the subject of the verb *is*.

3. <u>Being fifty years of age</u>, Jeb's father gets a cheaper car insurance rate.

Present participial phrase; functions as an adjective modifying *Jeb's father*.

4. The purpose of any enthusiastic marathoner is <u>to win.</u>

   Infinitive phrase; functions as a noun and as a subject complement.

5. <u>To reach the summit</u> was the climbers' ultimate goal.

Infinitive phrase; functions as a noun and the subject of the verb *was*.

6. <u>Neutered and regularly vaccinated</u>, a male dog has a better chance of reaching old age.

Past participial phrase; functions as an adjective modifying *a male dog*.

7. Thankfully, the pedestrians avoided the badly <u>shattered glass</u>.

Past participial phrase; functions as a noun and the direct object of *avoided*.

8. Any <u>interested and qualified</u> students should apply within.

Past participial phrase; functions as an adjective modifying *students*.

9. It is always better <u>to give</u> than <u>to receive</u>.

Infinitive phrases; function as nouns and subject complements.

10. Andrew decided <u>to go</u> home for the spring break.

Infinitive phrase; functions as an adverb modifying *decided*.

10.   Subordinate Clauses

1. Switzerland is one of the few countries in the world <u>where the trains arrive and depart on time.</u>

adjective

2. Address the letter to <u>whom you wish.</u>

noun

3. Promptly complete the homework <u>that is assigned to you.</u>

adjective

4. I had a relaxing weekend <u>because I had completed my final examinations.</u>

adverb

5. Raginder will proof my term biology essay <u>when he is good and ready.</u>

adverb

6. We think <u>that Patrick Dorn is the best candidate as our student representative.</u>

adverb

7. <u>Whichever career path she chooses</u> will be the correct one.

noun

8. The movie <u>that I saw on the weekend</u> featured Adam Sandler in a very unconventional role.

adjective

9. My mark was better <u>than the grade I received in the first term</u>.

noun

10. The visiting professor, <u>who has won a Nobel Prize in chemistry</u>, gave a

adjective

scintillating lecture on science and ethics.

11. <u>After they took a cruise down the Danube</u>, they ate goulash in one of

adverb

Budapest's best open-air restaurants.

12. <u>What you learned on the CRC station about the political race</u> is probably biased.

noun

11.   Sentence Types

1. Coincidentally, the convicts were wanted in British Columbia and in Nova Scotia, too.

    simple; declarative

2. Are you planning to stay in the residence during reading break?

    simple; interrogative

3. Several critics think *The Sun Also Rises* is Hemingway's best novel; a small minority of critics do not consider it to be a major work.

    compound; declarative

4. You must do it now!

    simple; exclamatory

5. The person who helped me carry the package to my car became my wife within a year.

    complex; declarative

6. Once Cronenberg achieved popular success, the Canadian director confounded his audience, and he began making more artistic films.

    compound/complex; declarative

7. As a newspaper reporter, Ernest Hemingway once wrote for *The Toronto Star*.

    simple; declarative

8. Dame Cicely was among the most renowned stage actors of her generation, yet she had no formal theatrical training.

    compound; declarative

9. The Pawalskis had venison steaks that Earl had stored in the freezer.

    complex; declarative

10. While I watched dumbfounded, Gillian entered the room and sat down, crushing the divan.

    complex; declarative

11. Drop your weapons, and come out with your hands up.

    compound; imperative

12. The Andersons ate moose hamburgers, and the Pawalskis consumed venison steaks that Earl

had kept stored in the freezer.

    compound/complex; declarative

Chapter 10: COMMON SENTENCE ERRORS

1.   Correcting Sentence Fragments

1. In the final moments of the game, our team's wide receiver dove for the ball and made the

    catch for a touchdown to win the game. (lacking a subject)

2. After I cook my famous rib recipe, most people say I should leave school and open a

    restaurant called Uncle Ricky's Rib House. (subordinate clause)

3. The sentence is complete.

4. No one from my hometown had come to Spuzzum Community College before I enrolled.

    (lacking a subject, subordinate clause)

5. After he checked for e-mail messages, Jason stayed up all night to finish his term paper.

    (subordinate clause)

6. While I stood on a jagged rock watching the glorious Tofino sunset and munched sunflower

    seeds, my heart began to lighten. (subordinate clause)

7. I became a contestant on the television show *Fear Factor* and completed my first task with

    an unsettled stomach. (lacking a subject and a verb)

8. In my darkest moments, I wish I had never been born. (lacking a subject and a verb)

9. Tammy wanted to see both Academy Award–nominated movies, but she only had the time

    and money to view one. (lacking a subject)

10. Any discussion of diseases requiring more research funding must include the major ones that

    kills Canadians, for example heart disease, cancer, and diabetes. (lacking a subject and a

    verb)

2.   Editing to Correct Sentence Fragments

Family reunions are definitely not my idea of a good time. At these events, I often do battle with judging parents, rude or inebriated uncles, ultra-nosy aunts (or ones who talk to me like I'm still three years old), and rug-rat nieces and nephews. Plus, I often end up eating fifteen different varieties of potato salad because most of my relatives are too cheap to buy a substantial meat dish. Wouldn't it be great if everyone chipped in about thirty dollars for a buffet restaurant? Then at least we would be sure to get a balanced meal—not to mention a little variety among Canada's major food groups.

Another family-reunion pet peeve of mine is the conversation, or lack thereof. As a college student, I'm forced to attend these dreaded affairs at the threat of having my income flow stopped immediately. After I get there, it seems that all assembled relatives must grill me on the standard topics— for example, my academic performance, my love life, career prospects, salary expectation in my field, and, of course, the reason for pursuing any line of work from the perspective of the chronically middle aged: sick leave, disability benefits, and pensions.

After I check my watch every thirty seconds, it's finally time to go. But wait! I have to say goodbye to every relative in attendance, which takes at least another half hour. If I don't, I'll be officially excommunicated from my extended family for the cardinal sin: thoughtlessness. By the time I get to my car, I'm thinking the once-in-a-lifetime party that every girl who I've ever wanted to date will be at is now over. Oh well, at least I saw ninety-six-year-old Aunt Agatha. Thank goodness family reunions only happen once every six months.

3.   Avoiding Comma Splices and Fused Sentences

1. Cape Bonavista, located on Newfoundland's northeast coast, is considered a possible site where John Cabot first landed in the New World in 1497.

2. The late Arthur Erickson, one of Canada's most renowned architects, was instrumental in the design of Simon Fraser University; however, he also gained international attention as the architect for the Canadian Embassy in Washington.

3. Paul Henderson scored probably the most dramatic goal in Canadian hockey history; it won the 1972 Canada–Soviet Hockey Series.

4. In the reproductive process of conifers, one male gamete fertilizes the egg, and the other degenerates.

5. Sir Wilfrid Laurier desired to correct abuses arising from fundamental changes in society, so he focused his attention on two bills, which ultimately resulted in his defeat.

6. Oscar Peterson's first music instructor, his sister Daisy, went on to become a respected piano teacher in the Montreal black community. Her later pupils included the fine jazz musicians Oliver Jones, Joe Sealy, and Reg Wilson.

4.   Review: Sentence Fragments, Comma Splices, and Fused Sentences

The following is a possible answer.

The fax machine was supposedly invented to help humankind; however, now it has become an instrument of marketing terrorism.

As the victim of innumerable junk fax transmissions, I have the greatest empathy for anyone who has been stalked by the sleeper cells of junk fax terrorists. My personal harassment started shortly after I purchased a fax machine and made the technological leap to a dedicated fax line.

Soon, my basement office was the receiving centre for a vast home-shopping network. All manner of commercial missives spewed off my fax rollers. Much to my amazement, I learned that I could buy oak flooring, get a cellphone for $0, subscribe to Internet magazines, and receive cash for my empty laser printer cartridges or old telephone system. I could also advertise my logo and a commercial message on "custom imprinted ceramic coffee mugs," pave my driveway at pre-season rates, buy discount vacations to Aruba, entertain clients at a billiards lounge/bistro, buy term insurance or mutual funds, and install a water cooler. And, if I needed cash to finance these "must-have" products and services, I could plug into a line of credit at "rock-bottom" interest rates with no questions asked.

Like many modern households, mine has a number of telephone lines: one for business, one for personal calls, one for the fax machine, and one for the Internet. Invariably, I was in the middle of an important work project or just about to sit down to dinner when one line's phone would ring and I'd pick up the receiver only to hear an annoying fax tone. The process continued every two minutes for each phone line in the house. Ironically, the junk faxes' advertisers boasted that they could increase my productivity by 50%, but they were decreasing it by 75% because I was constantly playing "musical phones," having to get up to answer junk fax calls.

While some faxes came from anonymous marketers, others provided phone numbers I could call to have my name removed from the master marketing list, but this struck me as highly unfair since the onus was on me to correct the problem.

What puzzled me most was how the fax marketers got my number in the first place. My research led to a telephone company vice president, who explained there were companies whose sole purpose is to create fax number lists. They obtain list entries by calling any random sequences of phone numbers. If they hit your number and get a fax tone, congratulations! You make the list. These companies then sell the list to telemarketing companies. I was told I could phone the number on the bottom of a junk fax to have my name removed from their list. This proved small consolation because the list compilers could have sold my phone numbers to other telemarketing firms.

Junk faxes are like a virus that's out of control, and the virus is living off my time and fax paper!

5.   Agreement of Subject and Verb, No. 1

1. My mathematics <u>teacher</u> **lives** near the university grounds.

2. In my opinion, the final two <u>chapters</u> of the book **are** the most thrilling.

3. The <u>students</u> on the fifth floor **win** the prize for the most outlandish costumes. **Correct.**

4. The Oscar-winning <u>actor</u>, along with her co-stars, **was** at a gala party after the ceremony.

5. <u>Laurel</u> and <u>Hardy</u> **star** in *Babes in Toyland* and *A Chump at Oxford*.

6. <u>Bacon and eggs</u> **was** the only thing the Levers would eat for breakfast on a Sunday morning.

7. <u>Every</u> man, woman, and child **has** the right to freedom from persecution.

8. Neither the <u>prime minister</u> nor his top <u>advisor</u> **knows** how to resolve the economic crisis.

9. <u>Somebody</u> **has** to stand up and make his or her voice heard above the crowd, but <u>nobody</u> **does**.

10. <u>Everyone</u> **realizes** that he committed the crime; however, without sufficient evidence, nothing can be done. **Correct.**

11. <u>None</u> of the crops **is** ready to be harvested.

12. Only <u>some</u> of the money from the bank robbery **has** been recovered.

6. Agreement of Subject and Verb, No. 2

1. The jury **deliberates** until a verdict is reached.

2. The jury **give** their separate decisions to a member who acts as the foreperson.

4. One-quarter of the public works budget **has been** allocated for snow removal.

5. About three-quarters of the shareholders **were** at the company's annual meeting.

6. There **are** three important reasons why I support Marika's proposal.

7. Hiding in the corner **were** the two cowering, terrified, pathetic thieves.

8. Our dogs, Lucy and Ace, **are** like kids to us.

9. His thinking **is** that the land values will go up after the factory opens.

10. The judges who **make** the final decision **do** not like Great Danes.

11. One of the issues we have to consider **is** how the development plan will affect wildlife.

12. Only one of the flight attendants **appears** to be on duty.

13. The news **has** not been good concerning her chances for a full recovery.

8. Irregular Verbs

1. Last night my brother-in-law <u>sang</u> the role of the barber in *The Barber of Seville*, a role he has <u>sung</u> many times in the past.

2. When the hunter saw the grizzly bear, he <u>froze</u> in his tracks.

3. Lucille <u>hung</u> the family portrait prominently in the den.

4. The convicted killer was <u>hanged</u> by the neck until he was dead.

5. After he was <u>bitten</u> by the salivating dog, Jerome <u>sought</u> medical attention at the nearest hospital.

6. I <u>dreamt</u> that the menacing dragon was <u>slain</u> by the valiant knight.

7. The bank robbers <u>hid</u> the money where it <u>proved</u> impossible to find.

8. Ted had not <u>risen</u> so early in the morning for years.

9. The punch was <u>drunk</u> before the last of the wedding guests had <u>left</u>.

10. The teenagers <u>dove</u> into the lake from the old train bridge even though they had been <u>forbidden</u> to do so on many occasions.

11. Jennifer <u>laid</u> the reference books on the top shelf last Wednesday.

12. The kidnappers had <u>lain</u> in wait for about an hour before their victims finally arrived.

13. He had <u>laid</u> the dozen red roses on the dining room table so that his fiancée would notice

them.

14. My Uncle Leo <u>lay</u> down for seven hours after he ate twelve helpings of Thanksgiving dinner.

15. The nude model had <u>sat</u> motionless for what seemed like hours while the art students sketched her.

9. Verb with *-es* and *-ed* Endings and Verbs Not to Omit

1. I **keep** my ski poles in the closet so I can easily find them.

2. Editing **requires** a good eye, a sharp pencil, and a complete library of up-to-date reference books.

3. I **take** half an hour to climb the long and winding hill on my bicycle, but the Canadian Olympic Cycling team **takes** only five minutes to reach the top.

4. The theatre manager **has** not had a night with such low attendance before, and he **doesn't** think it will happen again.

5. Last May, the controversial bill **was passed** after considerable debate in the provincial legislature.

6. In her native Guatemala, Ms. Rodriguez **practised** medicine for over fifteen years.

7. For years the labour leader had **championed** the cause of workplace safety.

8. My overdue rent cheque was **deposited** in the property manager's night mailbox.

9. Yesterday, the coach **escorted** the **hobbled** athlete to the dressing room for treatment on her hamstring.

10. After opening the box containing the swing set, Jessica's parents found the instructions **were** missing.

11. Consumer confidence **has** declined since the corporate scandals first struck.

12. The average hockey fan in Canada **suffers** a lot. He/she **doesn't** have much recourse when the local team **does** badly. In fact, a typical Canadian hockey fan probably **learned** to deal with ongoing frustration years ago. He/she **has** watched the local team fall to playoff defeat time and again. Dutifully, when a spate of injuries **strikes** during the regular season, he/she **watches** the **wounded** home team hobble along. The typical Canuck fan **has** no doubt **developed** countless strategies for coping with failure. To make matters worse, as player salaries **have** gone up, Canadian fan expectations **have** gone down.

10.   Verb Tenses

1.   At the end of James Joyce's short story "The Dead," the main character, Gabriel, **achieves** an epiphany. (The context of the sentence requires the literary present tense.)

2.   Sir Isaac Newton was instrumental in helping us understand that gravity **causes** things to have weight and fall to the ground when they are dropped.

3.   Sir Francis Bacon (1561–1626) **says,** "A prudent question is one-half of wisdom."

4.   Many of the communities **had not been** built when the power dam was constructed.

5.   While the Smiths searched for the missing girl along the beach, we **searched** behind the cabin.

6.   Bernice **wants** to pass the written examination next month.

7.   **Risking** his own life, he saved the drowning child.

8.   **Having studied** conscientiously for weeks, Elsa passed the final examination with ease.

9.   You will be late if you **take** the detour through Markham.

10. The rye bread has become moldy since I **took** it out of the package.

11. We had already eaten dinner when they **arrived**.

12. The actor **trained** in London, England, before coming to Niagara-on-the-Lake.

11.   Using the Subjunctive Mood Appropriately

1.   It is critical that the emergency-room physician **be** briefed on an incoming patient's condition.

2.   They insisted that the lawyer **print** copies of the uncle's will in triplicate.

3.   My neighbour wishes that she **were** the winner of the provincial lottery so that she could buy new windows.

4.   If Denis **were** the only man on earth, Stella would still not go out with him.

5.   She could run for the office of President of the United States if she **were** not born in British Columbia.

6.   Correct.

7.   We wish that our father **were** closer to Ontario so he could visit more often.

8.   The coroner's report recommends that a retaining wall **be** erected around the hairpin turn.

9.   The doctor urges that Jason **lose** weight to help lower his cholesterol.

10. Correct.

11. Correct.

12. It is required that the seller **present** himself or herself at the municipal office at 1 p.m.

13. I'd invest in real estate if I **were** a wealthy woman.

14. If he **arrives** late, I will give him a lecture on punctuality.

15. Despite our long personal history together, she greeted me as though I **were** a stranger.

12.   Active versus Passive Voice

Part 1

a)   The RCMP caught the escaped criminals in Lethbridge after a lengthy and dangerous chase. **OR** After a lengthy and dangerous chase, the RCMP caught the escaped criminals in Lethbridge.

b)   Each week, millions of North American viewers watched the domestic exploits of the Osborne family.

c)   The owner of the red sports car filed a lawsuit against the driver of the cream-coloured minivan who broadsided him.

d)   In certain parts of the world, people consider eating chocolate-covered insects a gourmet experience.

e)   A new Canadian telecommunications company gave Edward an entry-level management position.

Part 2

a)   The disease is divided into three main groups.

b)   Water is taken in through the roots of trees and plants and gradually released into the air through their leaves.

c)   The school was closed by heavy snowfalls.

d)   The new plasma television was designed by scientists to increase your viewing pleasure.

e)   During World War II, Canadians of Japanese descent were interned in camps within the Kootenay region of British Columbia by government officials. **OR** Canadians of Japanese descent were interned in camps within the Kootenay region of British Columbia by government officials during World War II.

13. Pronoun–Antecedent Agreement

Part 1

a) Everyone should do (his, her, <u>his or her</u>, their) part to reduce air pollution caused by automobile exhaust emissions.

b) If anyone wants to buy a ticket for the annual ski trip, (he, she, <u>he or she</u>, they) will have to do it by this coming Thursday.

c) Each dentist must ensure (he, she, <u>he or she</u>, they) carries adequate malpractice insurance.

d) The crowd stood up and cheered as (he, she, he or she, they, <u>it</u>) acknowledged the centre fielder's game-winning home run.

e) After the game, the capacity crowd slowly made (his, her, <u>their</u>, its) way to the various exits around the Rogers Centre.

f) The coach and the players were extremely tired after (his and their, its, <u>their</u>) long bus trip back from the game in Sault Ste. Marie.

g) Neither the team's general manager nor the players were prepared to share (his, their and his, <u>their</u>) feelings about the looming threat of a strike.

h) The faculty held (his and hers, their, <u>its</u>) Christmas party at a local country club.

Part 2

a) Each student learns the curriculum at their own pace.

— Students learn the curriculum at their own pace.

— Each student learns the curriculum at his or her own pace.

— The curriculum moves at each student's own pace.

b) Either Ellie or Nathan will have his essay selected as the best undergraduate essay for the previous year.

— Either Ellie or Nathan will have his or her essay selected as the best undergraduate essay for the previous year.

— Either Ellie's or Nathan's essay will be selected as the best undergraduate essay for the previous year.

14. Making Pronoun References Clear

1. Stella informed her mother that the telephone call was for her mother.

   Stella informed her mother, "The telephone call is for me."

2. In *Heavy Water*, Martin Amis ponders what it would be like if poets were highly paid and Hollywood screenwriters were not.

In Martin Amis' *Heavy Water*, the author ponders what it would be like if poets were highly paid and Hollywood screenwriters were not.

3. Hugh followed the steps in the chemistry experiments religiously, but the procedures didn't produce the reactions shown in the textbook.

Hugh followed the steps in the chemistry experiments religiously, but the experiments didn't produce the reactions shown in the textbook.

4. Marci drove her Toyota into a power pole, severely damaging the car.

Marci drove her Toyota into a power pole, severely damaging the pole.

5. In the article "A New Perspective on Biology," the author says that new research into the biological aspects of human personality is changing assumptions.

The article "A New Perspective on Biology" says that new research into the biological aspects of human personality is changing assumptions.

6. The movie holds its suspense right to the end. For example, in the final scene, the viewer never sees who fired the gun.

The movie holds its suspense right to the end. For example, in the final scene, the director never allows the viewer to see who fired the gun.

7. In bygone days, one (**OR** a person) could purchase a steak dinner for a dollar.

8. Archaeologists discovered a tool that was thousands of years old on the shore.

15. Using Pronoun Case Correctly

1. Miquel asked Rachel and (I, <u>me</u>) to accompany (he, <u>him</u>) and his wife to the concert.

2. Between you and (I, <u>me</u>), (<u>I</u>, me) think an outsider stole the money from the dorm piggy bank.

3. The driving instructor asked (he, <u>him</u>) to do a parallel park during the examination.

4. After much deliberation, the judges of the literary competition awarded the coveted literary prize to (he and I, <u>him and me</u>).

5. Despite our many differences, Chuck and (<u>I</u>, me) have resolved to behave in a civil manner while in public.

6. I'm not sure whether Don or (<u>I</u>, me, myself) will take the call from (he, <u>him</u>).

7. The lawyer forwarded a copy of the contract to Margaret and (I, <u>me</u>, myself).

9. The executive members of the marketing team—Davin, Aurturo, and (<u>I</u>, me)—gave the presentation to representatives of the client—Mr. Phillips, Ms. Edwards, and (she, <u>her</u>).

10. Let's you and (I, <u>me</u>) call the whole thing off.

11. (<u>We</u>, us) University of Victoria alumni are spread out all over Canada, but it is a little harder to find (we, <u>us</u>) Rhodes scholars.

12. Last semester, Cedric studied day and night, and (<u>he</u>, him) received much higher marks than (<u>I</u>, me).

13. Although our neighbours were a little shocked to see a college student out trick-or-treating, they gave the same number of treats to my four-year-old niece and (I, <u>me</u>).

14. After they became engaged, my sister and her fiancé asked (I, <u>me</u>) to give the toast to the bride.

15. The people in Oakville overwhelmingly voted to send (she, <u>her</u>) to represent (they, <u>them</u>) in Ottawa.

16.   Correctly Using *Who* and *Whom*

1. Whom did the students choose to represent them at the environmental conference?

2. Whoever attends the conference will need to make a serious commitment of his or her time, money, and energy.

3. At the conference, a scholarship prize is awarded to whoever makes the most compelling and convincing speech on a current environmental issue.

4. At present, organizers do not know who will be the keynote speaker this year.

5. There are several excellent candidates, and you can be sure that whomever the selection committee chooses will make an outstanding presentation.

6. Possible speakers can be narrowed down somewhat, since the committee plans to contact only people who are sympathetic to conference organizers' political agenda.

7. My stepmother, who is no longer alive, loved to travel to Portugal.

8. The relative to whom I owe my great sense of humour is my maternal grandmother.

9. Whom should I ask for information about pursuing a career in veterinary medicine?

10. Do you know Marika, who is the biology teaching assistant?

11. It was definitely she whom I saw at the reference library.

12. Happiness is there for whoever is willing to schedule time for it.

17.   Pronoun Review

I remember my first kayak rescue class as if it were yesterday. There were about eight of us, and we met at the university pool. First, everyone had to launch his or her small plastic kayak. Then, we all met at the centre of the pool, where our instructor, Dougal, coached us in some safety procedures. One technique was called the Eskimo Bow Rescue. I watched in horror as he demonstrated it with three other students. First, Barbara, the person role-playing the capsized person, had to stay in her kayak, then roll over and remain seated in the inverted boat, all the time completely submerged. While in this position, she reached her hands to the surface and thumped on the overturned hull to attract the attention of her rescuers. In this simulation, they were Theresa and William, who were supposed to be travelling with her. Once they noticed Barbara's banging, they were to meet around the capsized kayak to rescue her. As she blindly swept her arms back and forth, if everything went according to plan, her groping hands would somehow find a friendly bow, and use it to hoist her and her kayak out of the water with a flick of her hips.

This seemed horrifyingly dangerous to me. The weakness of the plan, which might work fine in a swimming pool where people were expecting something to happen, was that on the rolling open ocean, it would probably take a good deal more than thirty seconds for rescuers to notice you and then manoeuvre their boats into a rescue position. I doubt that anyone who has accidentally capsized at sea would patiently hang around upside down hoping that others would get to him or her before he or she ran out of air.

18.   Using Adverbs and Adjectives Correctly

1. The **powerful** Formula 1 racing car driven by Paul Tracy sped quickly around the track.
OR: The Formula 1 racing car driven by Paul Tracy sped quickly and **powerfully** around the track.

2. There are always employment opportunities for journalism graduates who can write **well**.

3. Skeptics were not **really** optimistic about the prospects for success of the young starlet's second marriage within a year.

4. **Relentlessly**, Gavin watched the horizon.

OR: Gavin **relentlessly** watched the horizon.

OR: Gavin watched the horizon **relentlessly**.

5. My dry-cleaned cashmere sweater felt very **soft**, and when I put it on, the garment smelled **fresh**.

6. He felt bad because his behaviour at Myra's party had so been so atrociously **bad**.

7. Of the six candidates we interviewed for the vacant human resources officer position, Eloise was by far the **best** applicant.

8. Mother Teresa was probably one of the **least** selfish people I studied in the entire history course.

9. All things considered, between the Dream and Shaq, I think Shaq was the **better** NBA centre.

10. We concluded that Pele was a **more** dominating athlete than Michael Jordan and that the great soccer player left his sport **more** gracefully than did the aging basketball star.

11. Edgar's younger brother, Speedy, is without a doubt the **laziest** person I know.

12. On the charity calendar produced by the Saskatoon Fire Department, it seemed that each month's featured firefighter was **handsomer** than the previous month's.

13. It becomes more and more **difficult** to find the missing child with each passing day.

14. Heathcliffe was so tired that he could **scarcely** get his work done.

15. The Winslows **have done nothing** to deserve the incredibly bad luck they've experienced over the past six months.

OR: The Winlows have never done **anything** to deserve the incredibly bad luck they've experienced over the past six months.

19.   Misplaced Modifiers

Part 1

a) Ted told the police officer investigating the accident **only** what he had seen.

OR: Ted told **only** the police officer investigating the accident what he had seen.

b) The new dormitory was **barely** finished when we moved in.

c) Some grocery concerns are trying to market cheese products **made out of soy** for health-conscious consumers.

d) The **unshaven and menacing** face of the man peering through the sliding door belonged to the cat burglar.

e) **Rarely** do people who enter careers such as daycare assistants become wealthy.

f) Statistics prove that **not** all serious traffic accidents are caused by drinking and driving; many are caused by drivers talking on cellphones while operating their motor vehicles.

g) It is a by-law infraction to walk your dog off a leash **within municipal boundaries**.

Part 2

Lawren Harris, a profound influence on three generations of Canadian painters, was a catalyst in the creation of the Group of Seven. Never has a group had **such a lasting impact** on the Canadian art scene.

Harris was from a family of great wealth. **After attending St. Andrew's College**, he went to the University of Toronto, where he was encouraged **by his mathematics teacher** to study art **in Berlin**. **Upon returning to Canada** in 1908, Harris, went on sketching tours of the Laurentians and the Haliburton area. **At the same time**, he drew and painted houses in downtown Toronto.

20.   Correcting Dangling Modifiers

1. Partying and playing computer games every day, his marks and reputation as a good student suffered.

> REVISED: Partying and playing computer games every day, he lost his reputation as a good student and his marks declined.

2. Our two weeks at the cottage went quickly, swimming and reading mystery novels.

> REVISED: We spent two fast weeks at the cottage, swimming and reading mystery novels.

3. To successfully fight a life-threatening disease or injury, determination and family support are required.

> REVISED: To successfully fight a life-threatening disease or injury, a person requires determination and family support.

5. After visiting the doctor, Jeff's lanced boil completely disappeared.

> REVISED: After Jeff visited the doctor, his lanced boil completely disappeared.

6. <u>While asleep on the airplane</u>, someone stole my complimentary copy of *Maclean's* magazine.

REVISED: While I was asleep on the airplane, someone stole my complimentary copy of *Maclean's* magazine.

7. Correct.

8. The puck, <u>inching across the goal line past the sprawling Red Wing goalie</u>, the crowd at the Air Canada Centre went wild.

REVISED: As the puck inched across the goal line past the Red Wing sprawling goalie, the crowd at the Air Canada Centre went wild.

9. <u>Travelling through the earthquake-ravaged region</u>, the effects of the devastation became evident.

REVISED: When we travelled through the earthquake-ravaged region, the effects of the devastation became evident.

10. <u>While attending a downtown theatre performance</u>, thieves broke into Ingrid's new Porsche.

REVISED: While she was attending a downtown theatre performance, thieves broke into Ingrid's new Porsche.

11. The tour bus returned to the hotel <u>after dinner was eaten</u>.

REVISED: The tour bus returned to the hotel after the passengers had eaten dinner.

12. Keep running <u>until the finish line</u>.

REVISED: Keep running until you reach the finish line.

13. Correct. (This sentence is correct if the meaning is that *they* were walking when they found the missing old man.)

OR: They found the missing old man walking near the beach trail. (Move the modifier to the end of the sentence, near *missing old man*, if the meaning is that the old man was walking when they found him.)

OR: When they were walking near the beach trail, they found the missing old man. (This makes the meaning absolutely clear.)

Chapter 11: PUNCTUATION

1. Commas with Coordinating Conjunctions to Link Independent Clauses, Commas with Compound Elements, and Commas with Introductory Words

1. The weather has turned chilly this September, so the leaves in the park have started to

change.

2. You can lead a horse to water, but you can't make it drink.

3. He paid the bill while Mary collected the coats, and they left the Chinese restaurant together.

4. Correct.

5. When filing for unemployment insurance, always bring sufficient identification.

6. Before opening a container of insecticide, ensure that you wear rubber gloves.

7. After longer introductory prepositional phrases, use a comma to indicate that the main part of the sentence is about to start.

8. While hiking in the Swiss Alps, he slipped on the icy surface and fell hundreds of metres to his death.

9. On Fridays, I have a beer at the student pub.

10. To verify the real father's identity, scientists conducted conclusive DNA testing.

11. By investing wisely in high-return stocks, Otto plans to retire midway through his senior year of university.

13. To tell the truth, I wish grandpa would quit driving.

2.   Commas in a Series and with Coordinate Adjectives

Part 1

a. The biology slide samples have been sorted, arranged, checked, and labelled.

b. When I have marked your examination paper, when I have tabulated the results, and when I have posted the final score, then you may leave my office.

c. At the family Muskoka resort, we discovered the air is wonderful, the scenery is spectacularly colourful, and the home-cooked meals are divine.

d. I especially enjoy eating around Christmas because at our house one can feast on turkey, stuffing, cranberry sauce, Nuts and Bolts snacks, pate, steak and kidney pie, plum pudding, and Aunt Edith's Christmas cake.

e. Like a true American, he wanted life, liberty, and the pursuit of happiness.

Part 2

a) She was an emotional, brilliant, brutally honest public speaker.

b) No commas are required.

c) I know that Malamutes are large, friendly, playful dogs.

d) No commas are required.

e) Getting a university degree or college certificate can be a long, discouraging, expensive process.

f) I woke up to find a sleek, shining silver Porsche Boxster in my driveway and immediately knew I was still dreaming.

g) He has been a true, dear, faithful friend through the difficult grieving period.

3.   Commas to Set Off Non-restrictive Elements

1. *A Jest of God*, which is my favourite Margaret Laurence book, is on Professor Ratke's reading list for the fall semester.

2. Jasmine, who has an interest in pottery, wants to major in fine arts when she transfers to university.

3. No commas are required.

4. The robbers, with large unmarked bills dangling out of their pockets, fled the bank.

5. No commas are required.

6. No commas are required.

7. Philip Roth's memoir, *Patrimony*, is the best non-fiction book I've ever read.

8. The Trans-Canada Trail, which passes through Burlington, is popular among ardent hikers.

9. Donovan Bailey, who is arguably the best sprinter that Canada has ever produced, won a gold medal at the 1996 Atlanta Olympics.

10. Finally falling asleep, Jennifer was soon awoken by a call confirming her Monday appointment at the sleep disorder clinic.

11. No commas are required.

12. The candidate, a political lightweight, hasn't a hope of winning the election.

4.   General Comma Uses, No. 1

1. Gillian has maintained a 75 percent average throughout her undergraduate studies; however, that academic record will not get her into the prestigious graduate school.

2. He was a very eccentric musician; for example, he conducted media interviews while buried up to his neck in sand.

3. In addition, he will be tutoring private students.

4. No commas are required.

5. Cellphone users, I think, must consider themselves important people.

6. Their popularity waning and their record sales plummeting, the band broke up.

7. Royal Roads University, not the University of Victoria, has an English garden.

8. The Canadian Minister of Foreign Affairs and International Trade, unlike her counterpart in Washington, issued a statement to the press after the conference.

9. No commas are required.

10. Yes, you can have a ten-minute coffee break midway through the seminar.

11. You paid your fall tuition installment, didn't you?

12. Yeats, on the other hand, is a very different Irish poet.

5.   General Comma Uses, No. 2

1. She said, "He would have died anyway."

2. No commas are required.

3. "It'll stop in due time," he says.

4. "But why," said Jeanne angrily, "did you not use Canadian quotations of some sort?"

5. On January 2, 1935, Prime Minister R.B. Bennett began a series of live radio broadcasts outlining a "New Deal" for Canada.

6. No commas are required.

7. Canadian singer and songwriter Sarah McLachlan was born in Halifax, Nova Scotia, in 1968.

8. Send your tax-deductible contributions to the Me Foundation, care of Me at 2819 Lakeshore Rd., Burlington, Ontario L6B 4M1.

9. The musical program at the convocation ceremonies includes The Island Pacific Brass Quintet with Richard Ely, Director.

10. No commas required.

11. Beyond, the rolling hills continued for kilometres.

12. I'm a lover; Jack, a fighter.

6.   Avoiding Unnecessary Commas

1. After staring down the batter, the pitcher wound up, and delivered a mean curve ball.

2. He cannot have hernia surgery, unless he loses weight, and unless he is willing to pay the

cost of treatment at a private clinic.

3. As almost every hockey fan knows, Paul Henderson, scored the winning goal for Canada in the 1972 Summit Series.

4. After spring break, the psychology professor returned the marked examinations, to her students.

5. A small number of historians think that, John. A. Macdonald, Mackenzie King, and Pierre Elliot Trudeau, are among the most influential Canadian prime ministers.

6. Confidentially, it was the first, high-stakes, murder investigation on which the rookie detective had worked.

7. Miraculously, it seemed, Sunji completed the exhaustive, biology examination within the allotted, two-hour time period.

8. Our lacrosse players triumphed in the closely, fought contest, and they eventually won the conference championship.

9. The old fire hall, that once was a heritage site, is now, unfortunately, slated for demolition.

10. He said, "Do not park in a space for the handicapped, unless you have an official sticker."

11. In my all-too-rare, leisure hours, I enjoy reading contemporary, humorists such as Steve Martin, Erika Ritter, and David Sedaris.

12. Updating the famous sports saying for a politically correct audience, the sportscaster said that, it is not over until the large-size woman sings.

7. Comma Review

Photographer, artist, and writer Peter Pitseolak, was born on Nottingham Island, Northwest Territories, in November of 1902, and he died September, 30, 1973. Just before his death, Pitseolak said, "I am telling the true things I know. I am not adding anything, and I am not holding anything back." Pitseolak's passion for telling the truth about his people, produced a stunningly, rich legacy of photographs, paintings, music, and writing. He took his first photograph in the 1930s for a white man who, fortunately, was too scared to approach a polar bear.

Apparently, in the early 1940s, while, working for fur traders, Pitseolak was given a camera from a Catholic, missionary. Then, with help from his wife Ageeok, he developed his very, first photograph in an igloo, using a flashlight covered with red cloth.

A leader in his Inuit community, Pitseolak realized traditional life was dying, so he decided to record its passing by writing diaries, notes, and manuscripts. As well, he drew Inuit customs and legends, and took countless evocative photographs.

Since his death, Pitseolak's remarkable photographs have given the world a unique first-hand account of the forces of twentieth-century change on the people of Baffin, Island. During the summer of 2001, a selection from the works of this master storyteller was exhibited at the Canadian Museum of Contemporary Photography.

8.   Semicolon or Comma?

1. The food at The Rude Waiter Restaurant was superb; the service was lousy.

2. She was an outstanding athlete, but her transcripts revealed that she was by no means a scholar.

3. He was the type of employee who was excellent at formulating strategies; however, he was not so good at actually carrying them out.

4. Alice Munro employs an oxymoron; hence, she underlines the fundamental contradiction in the heroine's predicament.

5. It is wise to plan early for your retirement; at the same time, you have to live for today.

6. Having a basic understanding of psychology is invaluable in the workplace; for example, it is helpful to know what motivates fellow employees.

7. David is very lineal in his thinking patterns (,;) while Marcella is a completely divergent thinker.

8. The sports awards dinner was attended by football players, including all of the linebackers, a defensive back, and the split ends; basketball players, including the centre, a point guard, and the water person; and hockey players, such as the goalie, her backup, and two forwards.

9. Our reading list in English 134.5 was rich in Canadian novels and included (,;) *Barney's Version*, *In the Skin of a Lion*, and *The Honorary Patron*.

10. Once the student painters had finished painting the living room, they moved on to the dining room.

11. Stephano would not miss an episode of *The Sopranos*, a dark (,;) but well-written and finely acted portrayal of the life of an extended mob family.

12. In conclusion, the Nanaimo Estuary is a rich and vital ecosystem (,;) that residents cannot

afford to lose.

9. Editing for Correct Comma and Semicolon Use

Part 1

a. In theory, the mayor's office can do a lot to ease the housing crisis; in practice, it can do very little.

b. Prime Minister Arthur Meighen once said, "Inflation makes misery unanimous; it is universal poverty."

c. Winning is not only a good thing; it is the only thing.

d. In the Edmonton Oilers' glory years, the team featured Mark Messier, a hard-nosed centre; Glenn Anderson, an incredibly fast skater; and Wayne Gretzky, thought by many to be the best player to lace on a pair of skates.

e. To paraphrase Woody Allen, death doesn't scare me; I just don't want to be there when it happens.

Part 2:

Lester Bowles "Mike" Pearson ( ) (1897–1972) was an athlete (,) war veteran (,) history professor (,) and gifted diplomat. His contributions to Canada are significant. Pearson served on Parliament Hill as prime minister from 1963 to 1968 (;) established the National Arts Centre (;) proposed the first UN peacekeeping force to address the volatile 1956 Suez Crisis (,) commemorated at The Peacekeeping Monument (;) and gave us our national flag (,) many thousands of which now fly throughout our country. Pearson headed the Department of External Affairs from 1946(,) after its tremendous wartime expansion under the brilliant Norman Robertson. As a politician (,) Pearson continued to use his diplomatic talents to make Canada a major partner in the new UN and NATO (;) in essence (,) he played a major role in developing Canada's world peacekeeping reputation. His 1957 Nobel Peace Prize medal is displayed in the main lobby of the Lester B. Pearson Building (,) headquarters of the Department of Foreign Affairs and International Trade.

10. Correct Colon Use

1. There are four kinds of men on campus: the handsome, the intelligent, the rich, and all the rest.

2. Pierre Elliot Trudeau said it best: "The army is a poor training corps for democracy, no matter how inspiring the cause."

3. One policy dominates the president's foreign policy on Iraq: regime change.

4. No colon is required.

5. Dear Dr. Liverwitz:

   I am writing to apply for the veterinary assistant position recently advertised in *The Globe and Tail* …

6. A minute of silence will be observed at 8:39 a. m. to honour the memory of the victims.

7. Despite his barren love life, he felt optimistic about his chances of getting a date, since the ratio of women to men in the community college was 8:1.

8. The core textbook for the sociology course is *The Challenge of Diversity: Multiculturalism in Canada*.

9. Hill, Lawrence. *Black Berry, Sweet Juice: On Being Black and White in Canada*. Toronto: HarperCollins, 2001.

10. No colon is required.

11. E.J. Pratt's "Towards the Last Spike" appears in *Literature in Canada: Volume 2*.

12. No colon is required.

11.   Comma, Semicolon, or Colon?

MEMO

To:	All Fitness Consultants
From:	Jeff Hackett, Marketing Manager, Family Fitness Corporation
Subject:	Members Wearing Tank Tops While Working Out
Copy:	Ms. Marion Wurlizter, Executive President
	Mr. Corky Weisner, Executive Vice President
Date:	October 5, 2006

As we discussed in our last meeting, there are too many patrons working out on exercise equipment while wearing tank tops; the practice cannot continue. First, this presents an extremely odious hygiene risk, and it could cause problems for us should health inspectors visit our premises. Second, Family Fitness Corporation wishes to present itself as a family-oriented fitness club; therefore, having predominantly young, scantily clad, and often steroid-enhanced bodybuilders on display does nothing to foster the Disney-like image we would like to project. Washboard abdominals, bulging pectorals, and rippling quads can be intimidating to the overweight general public. At present, we have a ratio of family memberships to young singles of 3:1, and I want very much to increase the number of family memberships.

I would like to convene a meeting for Thursday, August 10, 2007, at 10:30 a.m. to discuss the issue. Some topics we might discuss include the following: what constitutes a tank top, particularly how much sleeve remnant officially constitutes one; how we will communicate the policy, perhaps by dropping leaflets from passing airliners; and how we will enforce such a policy, maybe by hiring a S.W.A.T. team of tank-top police.

Please make note of your ideas relating to this pressing issue, and let me know if the appointed time is convenient for you; otherwise, I will have to book a different room. I look forward to seeing you at the meeting, properly attired of course!

Jeff Hackett

12.   Correct Use of the Apostrophe

1. The student's laptop was left on a table when he went to the men's washroom. ✓

2. Despite his parents' darkest worries, the job Jason wanted was right behind destiny's door. ✓

3. The **Wilsons** attended the Flames' game at Calgary's famous Saddledome. ✓ ✓

4. The women's book fair will be held at the president's home after Thursday's budget meeting. ✓

5. **Grant** and Joanne's garden is now in full and glorious bloom. ✓

6. In terms of elegance, the McLeod**'s** and the Rappenport's cottages are like night and day. ✓

7. Bess' most outstanding feature, according to her father, is her paternal grandmother's Slavic nose. ✓

8. Julian's brother was difficult to work with and constantly argued that his job duties were someone else's responsibility. ✓

9. Did you know that Maury's brother-in-law's law firm is handling the mayor's highly confidential paternity suit? ✓

10. In Damian's opinion, the crow's-**nests** of tall ships are the best places to view the harbour.

11. It's anyone's guess who won't attend the kids' high school reunion. ✓ ✓

12. Who's planning to audit our local M.L.A.'s exorbitant expense claims?

13.   Correct Use of Quotation Marks and Using Punctuation with Quotation Marks

Part 1

a.   As Albert Einstein said, "Great souls will always encounter violent opposition from mediocre minds."

b.   No quotation marks are required.

c.   "Military intelligence is a contradiction in terms," said Groucho Marx.

d.   In describing what sort of future the aging population will bring, David K. Foote states, "Writer Nicholas Kristoff offer[s] a gloomy view … of conflict between a minority of working young and a majority of retired 'greedy geezers.'"

e.   Alice Munro's vision of the contradictory nature of love is brilliantly rendered in her short story "Dulse."

f.   The mischievous journalist bet a colleague that he could naturally weave the phrase "bodacious yams" into one of his feature sports articles.

Part 2

e.   "To tell you the truth," says Uncle George slowly, "your father was a crook."

g.   I'll give you my personal definition of the term "previously owned automobile": an expensive clunker.

h.   The chief economist termed the trend an "inflationary spiral"; however, the Statistics Canada data did not support this view.

i. "Where are you staying?" Tony asks politely, meaning "when are you leaving?"

j. Marie Winn presents an opposing view: "The self-confessed television addict often feels he ought to do other things but the fact he does not read or have conversations means that those activities are no longer as desirable as television viewing."

k. According to the newspaper, the mobster testified at his trial that he was not the only one. (Remove the quotation marks and preceding comma since this is an indirect quotation.)

14. Using Other Punctuation Marks Correctly

Part 1

a. The coach asked us if we had it in us to win the game.

b. Please turn on your computer.

c. She will attend the convocation ceremonies when she completes all the requirements for her M.B.A.

d. Will there be anything about the major Elizabethan dramatists on the examination?

e. Run, I think the house is on fire!

f. For your research on Canadian broadcasting, will you visit the CBC station in Edmonton, AB? Maybe the headquarters in Toronto, ON? Or, perhaps it would be a good idea to tour the studio in Halifax, NS?

Part 2

a) Sir Frances Bacon **(correctly, as we now know)** realized that science could provide as much wonder as any magician with a wand.

b) Within the invisible—**yet perceptible**—walls of the barrio are several people living in too few houses.

c) Yet the serious writing students can learn much from the piece—**not only from its minor faults but also from its many strengths as a descriptive essay.**

d) The trouble with King Henry **(Henry VIII)** was that he had a mind of his own and an eye for the ladies.

e) The Alabama magazine reported that Toronto [*sic*] is the capital of Canada.

f) We should agree that global ecological catastrophes—**such as global warming, ozone depletion, and acid rain**—are mostly caused by OECD countries' oil, mining, timber, and heavy manufacturing conglomerates.

Chapter 12: SENTENCE STRUCTURE AND STYLE

1.   Avoiding Awkward Sentence Shifts

1. Ted was terrified while driving along the black-ice-coated 401 Expressway, for **he** saw everywhere the carnage and wreckage from previous motor vehicle accidents.

2. When **Dan and I** want to avoid the risk of mutual funds in an uncertain stock market, we purchase Canada Savings Bonds.

   OR: When you want to avoid the risk of mutual funds in an uncertain stock market, **purchase** Canada Savings Bonds.

3. Fifthly, Shakespeare alters the way in which Iago **gets** possession of the handkerchief.

4. Angelee raced to answer the telephone, but nobody **was** on the line.

5. During the long drive to the cottage, Sal told stories about his glory days as a rugby player while his girlfriend **slept** soundly.

6. I want to meet the manager when employment statistics are improving and companies **are** hiring.

7. Address the chairperson first, and then you will be acknowledged. **Correct.**

8. She detested dishonesty, and by her standards, all hypocrites **were offensive**.

   OR: She detested dishonesty, and by her standards, all hypocrites **offended her**.

9. At Blue Jays' games, it is an important part of a ticket taker's responsibilities to collect tickets from paying customers and **not** let any gatecrashers into the stadium.

10. If I were wealthy and Tony **were** here, we would immediately go to the student pub to imbibe our favourite beverage.

11. While travelling in Europe, I asked a local resident **which road to take** to get to the cathedral.

12. Correct.

2.   Mixed Constructions

1. By increasing the amount of time she devoted to studying anthropology, Elsa raised her mark two letter grades for the spring semester.

OR: Increasing the amount of time she devoted to studying anthropology raised Elsa's mark two letter grades for the spring semester.

2. After completing a rigorous program in microbiology at an Ontario institution, Garrett pursued his medical studies at a leading university in the Maritimes.

3. Because the explorers could not locate an entrance to the Northwest Passage, they abandoned their expedition.

   OR: The explorers could not locate an entrance to the Northwest Passage, so they abandoned their expedition.

4. News of the final cuts for the varsity field hockey team was delivered by the coach to each affected player.

   OR: The final cuts for the varsity field hockey team were made by the coach.

5. Bungee jumping is for people with more money than brains.

   OR: Bungee jumping can have tragic consequences if proper safety precautions are not taken.

6. Almonte, Ontario, is where basketball inventor, physician, and educator James A. Naismith was born.

   OR: Almonte, Ontario, is where the inventor of basketball, James A. Naismith, a physician and educator, was born.

7. Because Daphne was half an hour late, we missed the rap concert.

   OR: Daphne was half an hour late, which was the reason we missed the rap concert.

8. I saw the water tower from the cockpit of the glider.

3.   Using Coordination and Subordination to Fix Choppy Sentences

1. William Maxwell (Max) Aitken is also known as 1st Baron Beaverbrook, a financier, politician, author, and publisher. The son of a minister, Beaverbrook would later claim that his religious beliefs were the foundation of his success. He moved with his family to New Brunswick in 1880. A bright if not mischievous youth, the young Aitken showed a great love for acquiring money. He tried journalism and sold insurance before working as a legal clerk in Chatham, New Brunswick. At this job, he began a lifelong friendship with R.B. Bennett, who later became prime minister of Canada. In 1897, Max left law school to follow Bennett to Calgary, where Aitken operated a bowling alley and then moved to Edmonton before returning

to the Maritimes.

2. Eating is an important part of a sumo wrestler's preparation. Most wrestlers weigh more than 136 kg, and much of the weight is concentrated in their stomach and hips because this area generates the pushing power so important in sumo wrestling. The extra mass also acts as a shock absorber, allowing a wrestler to stay on his feet in spite of his opponent's efforts to topple him. But do not dismiss sumo wrestlers as slow, fat food addicts. Despite their enormous size, they possess agility, strength, speed, and balance.

3. There are three major stages in the process of making a good instructional video. The first stage is *pre-production*, in which students plan their videos on paper. Pre-production involves all the planning and continues until the day students take out the camera. When they handle the equipment, students are in the *production* stage. *Post-production* is the final stage. It involves pulling all the shots together and making sense of the video footage.

4. In the 1920s, investigators realized that it was the chromosomes that carried the genes and information of heredity. Much later, in 1953, a major breakthrough occurred in chemistry when James Watson and Frances Crick discovered the DNA (deoxyribonucleic acid) molecule. Made while they were working in Cambridge, this discovery disclosed the fundamental mechanism of how heredity really worked.

4.   Effective Coordination and Subordination

1. Electronic mail is an excellent tool for international communication; however, people responding to messages sometimes inadvertently transmit computer viruses.
2. Television is one technology that most Canadians have in common. Almost all of Canada's 12million households (99%) have television sets, which is more households than own automobiles (60%) and home computers (75%).
3. Although there were many well-equipped paramedics attending to her, the driver unfortunately died at the scene of the accident.
4. The prison guard, noticing that the convict's bunk was empty, sounded the alarm that a prison break had occurred.

5. While wearing my insulated vest and looking through high-powered binoculars, I observed the unidentified flying object.

6. While there are a number of procedures to follow, if you think you have been discriminated against or harassed by someone in your workplace, report it.

7. The Raptor's power forward was a rookie in the NBA, but he had a better understanding of the game than many veteran players.

8. Recently, the provincial government deregulated electricity prices, so the cost to consumers skyrocketed, but the governing party will pay dearly for the policy change when voters go to the polls in the next election.

9. While dieting can have many benefits, if you try to lose significant amounts of weight without consulting your doctor, you can deprive yourself of essential nutrients, which poses significant health risks.

10. My favourite movie that the Italian director, who is in his prime, has done since emigrating to America won an Academy Award.

5. Parallelism

1. The new geography instructor has eloquence, charm, warmth, humour, a breadth of subject knowledge, and outstanding teaching ability.

2. The movie *My Big Fat Greek Wedding* was funny, touching, well acted, intelligent, and enjoyable.

3. Our literature study group discussed, analyzed, questioned, and then paraphrased sections of Earle Birney's *David*.

4. The corporate executive faced his trial confidently, insisting that he was innocent and rejecting all offers of a plea bargain.

5. The sprinter won the European championship by intimidating her opponents and by using steroids.

6. The lawyer tried to bait witnesses with seemingly innocent questions and then expose inconsistencies in their testimony.

7. The prime minister spoke to the grieving relatives of the victims with unquestionable sincerity and with resolve to seek justice.

8. Thomas Hobbes, a pessimist, thought that life was "nasty, brutish, and short" and that every

man had a price.

9. A good after-dinner speaker must be confident and must display a good sense of humour.

10. The RCMP accused not only the district manager but also the company president of embezzlement.

11. Dilbert may not have been the prettiest car in the parking lot, but it was the most reliable.

12. One can pay by cash, Visa, Mastercard, or Interac.

6.   Needed Words

1. The rookie defenceman's salary is meagre compared to **the salary of** the all-star centre.

2. The Toronto Maple Leafs have a larger fan base than any **other** sports team in the Ontario capital.

3. Correct.

4. Margaret Atwood's work is more widely recognized than any other Canadian **writer's**.

5. Canada is as well regarded **as**, and no doubt more so **than**, any other nation contributing peacekeeping forces to the region.

6. The youngest dog runs for kilometres while the older dogs **run** for mere metres.

7. The university's chancellor is aware **of** and in agreement with the proposal to create a memorial garden.

8. The young racer's skis are as well polished as an Olympic **champion's**.

9. We saw **that** the movie, which was garnering outstanding reviews, was completely sold out.

10. The scholarship student spends countless hours studying, but other scholarship students **spend** less time.

11. The local company has always **promoted** and will continue to promote from within.

12. Mother gave her more praise than **she gave** you.

7.   Creating Sentence Variety

A musical virtuoso, Glenn Gould is best known for his brilliant and innovative interpretations of classical piano compositions. However, many people do not appreciate that he had a remarkably varied creative career, which also spanned recording, writing, producing radio documentaries, composing, and conducting.

Born in Toronto, where he lived all his life, Gould was only three years old when he demonstrated exceptional music abilities, including perfect pitch. Soon, he was playing his own compositions for family and friends, and then competing in a few music festivals. Never subjecting him to the life of a star prodigy, his parents carefully nurtured his talent. Until he was ten, Gould's mother was his only music teacher. At that time, he began lessons at the Royal Conservatory of Music in Toronto, studying organ, piano, and music theory. In 1946, at age 14, he was awarded a diploma with highest honours.

As a result of his concert appearances, CBC radio and television broadcasts, and recordings, Gould was known across Canada by the early 1950s. He made his American debut in 1955 in Washington and then New York. Included an unconventional program of composers, his performances were dazzling. He was signed to a recording contract the day after the New York appearance, and his first recording, an interpretation of J.S. Bach's *Goldberg Variations*, was released in 1956. It received critical and popular acclaim and became the best-selling classical record of that year.

8.   Effective Sentences Review

During his lifetime, Grey Owl was a trapper, author, imposter, and visionary conservationist.

Arguably, he did more to promote conservation in Canada than any other Canadian in the first half of the twentieth century.

Grey Owl's real name was Archibald Stansfield Belaney, and he was born in 1888, in Hastings, England. As a boy, Archie was fascinated with North American Natives.

Belaney sailed to Canada as soon as he was old enough to travel. By living with the Ojibwa of northern Ontario, he learned about the wilderness and soon began presenting himself as the son of a Scot and an Apache.

Though he lied about his Native heritage, all of his presentations were not fabrication. Grey Owl, his Native name, sincerely worked for preservation of the beaver and their sensitive habitats. For example, he kept two beaver called Jelly Roll and Rawhide at his northern Ontario home. However, he later moved west. In 1931, Grey Owl boarded a westbound train with Jelly Roll and Rawhide—travelling to Manitoba's Riding Mountain National Park and a cabin that was built especially for him on the shore of Beaver Lodge Lake.

Grey Owl also nurtured his writing career and made speaking tours to Europe. By posing as a Native person during a time when Europeans held romantic images of Canada's first peoples, he found his ideas about protecting the environment were better received.

After Grey Owl's death in 1938, the press discovered his English birth, and headlines such as the following appeared: "GREY OWL HAD COCKNEY ACCENT AND FOUR WIVES."

9.   Wordiness: Eliminating Redundancies, Avoiding Unnecessary Repetition, and Cutting Empty or Inflated Phrases

1.   The company vice president must catch an 8:30 p.m. flight from the Vancouver airport.

2.   At the meeting, he had a unique proposal, but he presented it in a soft voice, so he was asked to repeat it.

3.   The circular pool was not good for swimming laps.

4.   I conclude from experience that cooperation is the most basic requirement of any successful team.

5.   Today, it is unique to find someone who can write so eloquently and understand modern telecommunications technology so profoundly.

6.   Many working people voted for Richard Nixon in 1972 because his tax plan still allowed them to realize the American dream.

7.   The octopus slowly swam past the eel.

8.   She consistently championed the basic principles of free speech and personal freedom.

9.   Essentially, the Montreal Expos are a threatened baseball franchise.

10. As the only surviving relative, Quan will inherit about two million dollars on his great uncle's death.

11. Because the rotating home has a unique design and materials, it is about 30 percent more energy efficient than a traditional home. This is if you do not turn the home. If you use the house's rotation potential and track the sun, it will be even more energy efficient. In fact, dome homes currently in Europe have been hooked up with solar panels, and a few even use computers to track the sun and maximize solar-power potential. Such computer-controlled solar heating systems also allow windows to collect passive solar heat. In the summer, the computer turns the home away from the sun.

10.   Eliminating Empty or Inflated Phrases

Part 1

a.   After discussions between representatives of the regional offices and central administrative services, senior management has decided that layoffs are not currently a viable option.

b.   She will not travel outside the country on business because her father is battling a serious illness.

c.   To succeed in the organization, a manager must delegate responsibility and write coherent memoranda.

d.   There has been a slight delay in the processing of your refund because of improvements we are making to our computer system.

e.   The lawyer has repeatedly said that all she ever wanted was a settlement that would give the family the economic security they need to pay her client's future medical bills.

f.   If her unemployment insurance expires, she will get a temporary job until she can find a position in her field.

g.   He was able to get work as a floral delivery person even though he had a drunk-driving conviction.

h.   Behavioural research shows that ducks tend to quack if they are disturbed by humans.

i.   They have exceeded the deadline, but they are completing the required work quickly.

j.   University was not the best option because she likes to drink and party.

Part 2

We have reviewed the admissions policy and concluded that, because more candidates are applying than we currently have space for, we must increase the minimum acceptable standard so that Admissions personnel can process applications quickly. The new admissions policy will begin on the spring deadline and continue until the number of applications decreases. This was our only viable option.

11.   Simplify Sentence Structure/Revise Wordy Sentences

1.   Petra's failure to submit assignments on time indicated her poor attitude towards learning.

2.   The rescue workers advanced slowly towards the trapped miners, and the minimal progress troubled doctors concerned about the victims' physical and mental health.

3. Brian secretly dreams of living like Hugh Hefner.

4. You have many opportunities to improve your final biology assignment by doing make-up assignments.

5. My mother hopes that I will continue studying Canadian literature in graduate school.

6. The federal government commissioned an independent research firm to study extensively the physical fitness of Canadian post-secondary students.

7. My father taught me never to gulp wine or eat peas with a butter knife at expensive restaurants, especially when he was paying the bill.

8. A thief wearing jeans and a burgundy coat stole my wallet.

9. The 90-kilometre-long road from Wiarton to Tobermory passes through an Ojibway reserve.

10. Confidently, Marcie entered the interview room.

11. The all-star point guard cocked her wrist and shot the title-winning basket in the dying seconds.

12. The world-renowned, Nobel Prize–winning chemist will speak in the five-hundred-person lecture theatre.

Chapter 13: USAGE

1. Appropriate Language: Avoiding Jargon, Pretentious Language, and Euphemisms

1. His main interest was in writing avant-garde poetry, and when he met a compatible woman, a meaningful relationship was the logical next step.

2. Since Enid is broke, she has economized by buying a used car.

3. Enemy forces conquered the area with few civilian casualties and then retreated.

4. They completed judging on *American Idol* by ranking candidates according to published rules and choosing the best contestant.

5. The short, deaf old man has died.

6. Today, the victims of the terrorist bombs were buried in a memorial garden.

7. Bob, an alpha-geek, was particularly sensitive to harsh, cluttered designs on websites.

8. Ed McDougal of our Winnipeg office will meet with management on the best strategies for growing our business in today's difficult economy.

9. The plumber tried to fix the leaky toilet by using a plunger.

2. Appropriate Language: Avoiding Slang, Regional Expressions, and Informal Language

For letter format, see the letter model in section 13-1D of *Checkmate*.

Dear Harry,

I am writing to apply for the research position advertised on www.wowjob.ca.

Over the past three years, I have worked as a researcher for various education professors at the University of Waterloo. A large part of my work involved assisting various professors in their research to determine which teaching strategies and materials are used within the educational community. I was the go-to person for administering research surveys and questionnaires by mail, telephone, and e-mail. Plus, I proofread final analysis reports, gaining a reputation as one incredible editor. My work often required contacting main administrators at schools, school board offices, colleges, universities, and departments of education.

I have also helped conduct market analysis research projects in the business world. A recent project I worked on involved surveying telecommunications decision makers to ascertain their customer needs.

While a summer intern with the British Columbia Ministry of Education, I helped file in the Assessment Branch.

My writing skills are superb. To give you just one example, this past academic year, I won a prize for the best undergraduate essay, and I have published two short stories in the campus magazine.

I'd love to meet you in person and tell you all about my qualifications.

Sincerely,

Enc.

cc Professor Edward Bennie

3. Avoiding Sexist Language

1. The councillor threatens to sue anyone who even suggests she might be influenced in her voting patterns by developers.

2. Mr. Hilderbrant III, Q.C., and Mrs. Hilderbrant were among the honoured guests at the head table of the charity ball.

3. He refuses to listen when I want to discuss our relationship.

4. Runners wanting to compete in the 10 K event must bring their entry forms and fees to the recreation centre office by Thursday at 4 p.m.

5. The boys hadn't seen each other for years and talked incessantly.

6. The project editor is responsible for ensuring that all contributing authors complete their chapters by the appointed deadline.

7. Please give registrants a certificate as soon as they complete the course.

8. The typical college student is concerned about the steadily rising cost of tuition.

9. If any student is dissatisfied with the fairness of a paper's grading, he or she can have it reviewed by a faculty representative.

10. As they progress in their studies, graduate students specialize in their fields of study.

11. The veteran journalist regretted that the newspaper didn't have the staff to adequately cover school board issues.

12. Mr. Singh was furious when the mail carrier took the parcel intended for the courier despite the fact he had posted a note indicating not to do so.

4. Improving Sentences: Exact Language, Concrete Nouns, and Active Verbs

1. It was our first vacation to a developing country, and we found that the capital city had many homeless people.

2. The aloof neighbour complained to a by-law officer every time the elderly lady's dog barked.

3. The two-bedroom bungalow had a garden teeming with tulips, daffodils, and roses.

4. People gave high ratings to five items on the survey, and this positive feedback will need to be discussed at our next meeting.

5. After crashing into the meridian, the car skidded along the wet passing lane as the driver swerved to narrowly miss a stalled cement truck.

6. Nobel laureate Desmond Tutu gave a compelling speech on forgiveness.

7. Death is an unpopular topic for dinner conversation.

8. Denying a political prisoner access to a lawyer violates his or her legal rights.

9. The British soldiers inside Fort Detroit were intrigued by the new sport, so the gates were opened and they watched Chief Pontiac and the Ottawa play lacrosse.

10. Correct—unless you know what team (basketball, hockey, etc.) and can be more specific.

11. Donald's doctor assured him that the test results were accurate.

12. The centre fielder hit the ball out of the park for a record-setting home run, and the wealthy cartoonist who paid millions of dollars for the previous record-setting ball lost his investment.

5.   Using Standard Idioms

1. I intend **to do** my income tax when I receive all of my T-4 slips from my previous employer.
2. Desmond told me to **be sure to** include a bibliography with the history assignment.
3. Bruce Springsteen is **different from** all the other aging rock stars playing the Air Canada centre this fall.
4. Get that dog **off** the sofa!
5. The teaching assistant recommended **that she do** a prerequisite course in cellular biology.
6. The student painters **agreed** to do the entire living room for $400.
7. Calvin filed an insurance claim of $200 **with reference to** the damage sustained during the flood of 2000.
8. You must comply **with** the posted speed limits, especially in school zones.
9. Having linoleum or hardwood as flooring is preferable **to** shag carpeting when one has dogs that spend a lot of time in the basement.
10. I will suggest **that he do** the work immediately.
11. His batting stance was superior **to** that of any other player on the minor league team.
12. The retirement party will culminate **in** a version of "For He's a Jolly Good Fellow."
13. Melvyn was associated **with** the notorious motorcycle gang Satan's Geezers.

Shelley was the type of mother who would do anything for her children.

6.   Avoiding Clichés and Mixed Metaphors

Part 1: Clichés

1. <u>dead as a door nail</u>

The cyclist was already dead when the officer arrived at the scene of the accident.

2. <u>straight as an arrow</u>

At the athletic banquet, the linebacker went directly to the buffet table where prime rib was being served.

3. <u>first and foremost</u>

With any wedding, the primary responsibility of the master of ceremonies is to remember the names of the bride and groom.

4. for all intents and purposes

The socialist, bilingual bookstore is virtually bankrupt.

5. step in the right direct

It was an astute decision when the government appointed a local parent to oversee cuts in the school board budget.

Part 2: Metaphors

1. buttered your bread, so now you must lie in it

   By cheating on the examination you've **made your bed, so now you must lie in it.**

2. Pandora's box of worms

   If you start complaining about dormitory noise when you're not the quietest person yourself, you'll be opening a whole **can of worms**.

3. hand in hand

   According to our physical education instructor, a sound mind and a sound body go **together**.

4. grab the bull by the horns and run with it

   When it comes to completing an essay on time, you just have to **grab the ball and run with it**.

5. marched to the beat of a dead duck

   The eccentric impressionist painter **marched to the beat of his own drum**.

Chapter 14: MECHANICS AND SPELLING

1. Spelling, No. 1

1. The beautiful **foreign** student mistook my **compliment** for an insult, so my first attempt at communication with her was extremely **disappointing**.

2. It would be extremely **wasteful** when **dining** out to order an **outrageously** priced meal and then eat only half of the food.

3. He is not the **heaviest** person I know, but he certainly will be **paying** for his obesity in later years with **weight-associated** problems that **affect** general health.

4. **All together**, the break-ins at the north campus **dormitory occurred** a **comparatively** few number of times.

5. Term **papers** are to be **submitted** with **appendixes** that **thoroughly** explain any relevant background information.

6. There are several **criteria** that must be met before a student can **register** for the senior-level English **course**.

7. Nelson Mandela is **truly** one the great **heroes** and public speakers of our generation—a man **whose** speaking voice brings tears to the eyes of some and raises others to action.

8. Like all well-written Elmore Leonard novels, the plot action builds to a climactic crescendo, and then the author presents an **ingenious** and **unexpected** resolution.

9. In the late 1960s, tie-dying T-shirts and wearing long **hair** were common **phenomena** among young people.

10. The **suddenness** of Tony's mother's death has left his father in deep confusion and unsure **whether** burial or cremation would be the best option.

11. **Gauging** from the few people who attended on this **occasion**, Philip is not an **extremely** popular person on campus.

12. My new girlfriend is a **lovable** person, **possessing** great **evenness** of **temperament** and even greater **keenness** of mind.

2. Spelling, No. 2

In Bram Stoker's *Dracula*, **there** is a complex **presence** of the "**foreign** other" [1]—those **individuals** who are not the Western, Christian, white middle- or upper-class male. Dracula, a "monster" and **foreign man** who threatens the Western male's identity, is **ultimately destroyed** despite his brute strength and **abundant resources. Similarly**, the female **heroine**, Mina, who uses her "male" skills to lead the British male characters to Dracula, is **ultimately reverted** to a domestic position that does not threaten Western patriarchy. The novel's final image of men reassures British male supremacy by **glorifying their** duty of **protecting** both women and the English nation as a **whole**. This **problematic ending** demonstrates that the British male characters must **ultimately** displace these "foreign" powers (good and evil) in order to **affirm their** fragile masculine identity, **which** is **based** on a patriarchy that must place males above the "**foreign**" other. To gain **patriarchal "regeneration"**—Anne McClintock notes that Britain mapped its **dysfunctional** concept of patriarchy onto its colonies, therefore **reinventing** the tradition of the paterfamilias **where** the British male was the father figure (McClintock 239–240)—the novel's male characters **seek** to destroy the foreign male, **thereby asserting their** masculine identity and British **dominance**. Also, the novel's **heroine**, Mina, is a complex woman who **possesses** maternal **abilities** and "male" skills; the British male characters are **unable** to **conquer** Dracula without her. However, the novel **consistently** demonstrates the male need to control women and **to** undermine **foreign** ability **in** order to **assert their** own **male** identity.

_____

[1] In reference to Edward Said's concept of Orientalism, and also in a specifically feminist context, Meyda Yegenoglu demonstrates how "the very desire to penetrate the veiled surface of 'otherness' is constitutive of hegemonic, colonial identity" (Yegenoglu i). She recognizes that "the figure of the Oriental woman has functioned as the veiled interior of Western identity, she calls into question the dualistic conceptions of identity and difference, of East and West" (Yegenoglu i). Hence, any Western portrayal of "otherness" symbolizes not only conditions in the East but also those in the West.

3. Using Hyphens Correctly

1. Correct.
2. After carefully weighing the income and daycare options, my **brother-in-law** has decided to become a **stay-at-home** dad.
3. The **eighteen-year-old** gang member was becoming well known to local police.
4. To make a liquor purchase at the **duty-free** shop, one has to be at least nineteen years old.

5. Lenore was able to rent a **bed-sitting** room with a **fold-out** bed in a **turn-of-the-century** house near the campus.
6. My foster father is poor at decision making and cannot make up his mind whether he wants to rent a **one-**, **two-**, or **three-bedroom** apartment.
7. About **one-third** of the **seventy-eight** elk in the herd had the **life-threatening** illness and had to be destroyed.
8. **Ex-premier** Davis was among the **all-powerful** people at the **mid-July** political fundraiser.

9. The **semi-invalid** young man painted the most richly detailed and lifelike picture of a Pacific Rim sunset that I have ever seen.
10. Although a **self-proclaimed** champion of human rights, the **president-elect** has sweeping powers that could make him a **quasi-dictator**.
11. Once the upholstery on our old orange sofa started to show its age, we decided to recover it with a **neutral-coloured fabric**. Then, we replaced our **hall lamp**.
12. When the contract of the Raptors' backup centre expired, the team made a strong bid to **re-**

sign him.

4.   Capitalization

1. **W**hat a pity that **B**ern, **S**witzerland dropped out of the competition for the upcoming winter **O**lympics.

2. Our Christmas **F**rench examination will be held on Tuesday, December 20, at 3:30 p.m.

3. My **u**ncle always complains that fireworks on Canada **D**ay are a waste of time and money.

4. Last **S**aturday, Don Cherry had an interview with **T**he **G**reat **O**ne during his "Coach's Corner" segment on **CBC**'s *Hockey Night in Canada*.

5. Each time Damon visited his doctor on Danforth **A**venue in Toronto, he made a point of stopping at the Athenian Garden **R**estaurant for a feed of **G**reek food.

6. The **a**cting **m**ayor visited an **e**xhibition of modernist painting at the Vancouver Art Gallery.

7. A valuable information source for any essay on **t**he **h**istory of **w**omen's **s**ports in Canada is *The Canadian Encyclopedia*. Here, one can learn about the great women's basketball team the Edmonton **G**rads, more formally known as the Commercial Graduates **B**asketball **C**lub. During the period from 1915 to 1940, the **G**rads sported an incredible 93 percent victory record. In 1924, the team played 6 games in conjunction with women's **O**lympics held in **P**aris. In 1926, the Grads won the **F**rench and **E**uropean **c**hampionships and later played 9 games in conjunction with the 1936 Berlin **O**lympics. **D**r. **J**ames Naismith, the **C**anadian-born inventor of basketball, once said, "**T**he Grads are the finest basketball team that ever stepped out on a floor."

5.   Using Abbreviations Correctly

1. After Madeline Deter completed her M.B.A. at Harvard University, she was appointed Chief Financial Officer at CTV.

2. Dr. William C. Gibson, Chancellor of the University, will welcome graduates and their guests to the convocation.

3. The Anthropology 321 professor told her students that the first specimens of Java Man were found in 1891 and 1892 C.E.

4. My doctor prescribed some antibiotics for my severe cold, and I took the first dosage in the afternoon when I got home.

5. Our theatre reservations are for 4:30 p.m., and the cost of each ticket is $89 for a balcony

seat.

6. The heavyweight championship fight was held around 1918 and featured Joseph "Sweat Glands" Palooka versus Samuel "Bonecrusher" Smith.

7. The Prime Minister's plane will land at J.F.K. Airport in New York City, New York, in the morning; in the afternoon, he will give a speech to the UN Security Council, and in the evening he will attend a dinner hosted by Canada's representative at the UN, Guillermo Rishchynski.

8. Correct.

9. When he arrived at the unemployment office, he discovered he did not have a record of his social insurance number.

10. Correct.

12. In the botany experiment, we observed that the plant had grown twenty-three centimetres over the two-week period.

6.   Using Numbers Correctly

1. Thirty-two people were killed in the sinking of a Greek ferry last September.

2. For the August 15 performance of Shakespeare in the Park, there was a paid attendance of 178, so the total profit was $4 895.

3. Mackenzie King's greatest legislative achievement was the Industrial Disputes Investigation Act of 1907, but he is perhaps best remembered for introducing conscription for the defence of Canada in 1940.

4. Act V, Scene iii in *Taming of the Shrew* opens with Bianca saying, "Good sister, wrong me not nor wrong yourself."

5. On September 30, 2002, the federal government announced an environmental policy that would call for the banning of truck traffic on the 401 highway.

6. Page 9 was the end of the fax transmission; there was no page 10.

7. The invitation states that the book launch will be held at 17 Government St., commencing at eight o'clock in the evening.

8. Only 75 percent of the 130 000 Grade 10 Ontario secondary school students who took the literacy examination passed.

9. Ottawa is host to one of the world's largest resident diplomatic corps: 105 embassies and high commissions, of which seventy-three are from developing countries.

10. Correct.

11. The 15 m Canadarm functions like a human arm and has six joints: two at its shoulder, one at its elbow, and three at its wrist.

12. Of the 21 000 000 people in the small Eastern European country, only 275 000 voted for the leftist candidate.

7.   *Italics* and <u>Underlining</u>

1. Teresa Sandhu will give a short oral presentation based on her M.A. thesis, "Social distance and the pidginized speech of Punjabi women in British Columbia."

2. In *Calvin and Hobbes,* Waterson often makes a wry comment on the human condition through the voices of his cartoon characters.

3. It is unfair to compare Morley Callaghan's short story "A Cap for Steve" with his longer works such as the novel *A Fine and Private Balance*.

4. Fans of CBC's *Hockey Night in Canada* were chagrined to learn of Ron MacLean's departure as host of the popular sports show.

5. Gordon Lightfoot's affecting song "The Wreck of the Edmund Fitzgerald" tells about the sinking of the *Edmund Fitzgerald* in Lake Erie.

6. The student cinema will hold an Orson Welles film festival featuring, of course, *Citizen Kane* (1941), as well as Welles' lesser-known works, such as *The Magnificent Ambersons* (1942), *The Lady from Shanghai* (1948), and *Touch of Evil* (1958).

7. The painting *Church and Horse*, 1974, by Canada's Alex Colville perfectly complements Alice Munro's classic short story "Boys and Girls" in the anthology.

8. At a vertically challenged four feet and five inches in height, Calvin suffers from a *folie de grandeur* if he thinks he can become a starting centre in the NBA.

9. When I was dealt a 7 at Casinorama, Delores called me lucky, but her definition of *lucky* and mine are at odds since I lost $10 000.

10. The *Globe and Mail* has a regular feature called "Facts & Arguments," which I often find enlightening or amusing.

11. My neighbour strongly indicated that he would not call the police again.

12. The author of the article in *Maclean's* suggests that the South American general's aide-de-camp was a conspirator. (Note: Depending on the dictionary consulted, *aide-de-camp* may not be considered part of the English language and, therefore, italicized, making the original sentence correct.)

8.   Spelling and Mechanics Review

Natalie Singh

1412 Prince Dr.

Markham, ON

M3H 2L4

(905) 945-3876

e-mail: nsingh@presto.com

OBJECTIVE: To become an investigative journalist specializing in educational issues.

SKILLS

- Ability to research thoroughly and meticulously using a wide range of traditional and new media.

- Proficiency in analyzing information and statistical data.

- Excellent writing and editorial skills.

- Strong project management skills; able to complete complex assignments on time.

- Highly computer literate, having mastered many word-processing, graphics, and desktop-design programs.

WORK EXPERIENCE

- Research Intern. University of Waterloo. April-September 2001-2003. Assisted in educational research projects for three professors.

- Administrative Assistant Intern. British Columbia Ministry of Education. April-September 2000-2001. Helped administer and improve a computer-records filing system in the Assessment Branch.

- Market Research. Ed Lottenville Group. March-October 1999. Conducted telephone research to determine needs of decision makers in the telecommunications industry.

ADDITIONAL EXPERIENCE

- Adult Literacy volunteer tutor. Taught basic literacy skills to young adults who had severe developmental problems.

EDUCATION

- Carleton University, Ottawa, Ontario. Bachelor of Arts (Journalism) expected in 2004.
Activities: Ocean kayaking, reading, yoga.

PUBLICATIONS

- "Circular Home." *The Gainville Star*, December 15, 1999, p. E2.
- "Insulating Your Basement." *Canadian Home Life*, Spring 1998, p. 52

References available upon request.

Chapter 15: ELL (ENGLISH LANGUAGE LEARNERS)

1.   Articles

1. He was **an** unlikely candidate for the election.

2. There was a gorgeous sports car in the display window. **The** car was black.

3. Jason wore a powder-blue shirt on his first day of work. It was **a** permanent-press shirt.

4. After trying to lift the enormous rock without bending, he needed **a** hernia operation.

5. Sometimes it is difficult being **an** only child.

6. **The** book you requested last Wednesday is now available at **the** special orders desk.

7. If college does not work out, you could always enlist in **the** armed services.

8. Cyril invited me over to play **a** game of chess.

9. The cover of Erika Ritter's new book says that it was shortlisted for **the** Writers' Trust Non-Fiction Prize.

10. If you believe **the** latest issue of *New Brunswick Business*, there is not **a** richer man in **the** province.

11. For recreation she plays **a** little hockey on **the** weekend.

12. Snakes are reptiles.

2.   Editing for Correct Articles

Architect Douglas Cardinal was born in Calgary, but grew up on **a** farm outside Red Deer, Alberta. His mother predicted he would be **an** architect—even as **a** young boy he loved to construct things with building blocks. His father was **a** game warden whose deep love of nature was **a** part of his Blackfoot heritage. He showed his son **the** beauty of **the** land and taught him about **the** ways in which nature solves many problems.

Douglas Cardinal studied architecture at **the** University of British Columbia and **the** University of Texas. He opened **an** architectural office in Edmonton in 1967 and produced **a** varied but innovative body of work. He has designed **the** Edmonton Space Sciences Centre, schools, churches, homes, and many other buildings. His buildings are unique because of their curving shapes, which resemble **the** Canadian landscape.

Douglas Cardinal's architectural firm was one of the first to use **a** computer-aided drafting system (CAD). Arguably his greatest design accomplishment is **the** Museum of Civilization in Hull, Quebec. This building plays **a** key role in our nation's cultural life, housing artifacts that help Canadians learn about their past. For example, **the** museum features **a** great hall filled with totem poles.

Without **a** doubt, Cardinal is one of **the** most famous architects in Canada, and **a** supremely gifted artist.

3.   Helping Verbs and Main Verbs

1. The town councillors **have** asked the person applying for regional manager to be at the meeting.

2. We **were** planning a trip to Fredericton next summer.

3. I will have **done** all the assigned questions for geometry by the course deadline.

4. Today, my three-year-old nephew **has** eaten five helpings of spaghetti at one sitting.

5. My landlady is **being** a pain in the neck.

6. Arnold's father **has** been going to the same mechanic for ten years now.

7. Correct.

8. I **am** working on the term essay that counts for fifty percent of our final mark.

9. Canadian television audiences will **have** been watching CBC programs for sixty years in 2012.

10. My parents are **intending** to take a trip to Greece when they retire.

11. In some commentators' eyes, Obama and Putin are **being** hailed as champions of the war against terrorism.

12. **Have** you ever **seen** anything so incredible at a hockey game before?

13. Miles complained that we never **took** his contributions seriously during the entire term.

14. Correct.

15. The dunce will **have** been standing in the corner for five hours in about two minutes.

4. Editing Helping Verbs and Main Verbs

I will always remember my first trip through the Rockies. I must **have** been about ten at the time. As I recall, my mother **had** been planning the trip for about a year. My father **was** continually taking summer courses at university, so the trip gave him time to be alone and concentrate on his studies.

We boarded the train in Vancouver late at night and, as always, my sister **was** cranky because she **didn't** get enough sleep. Soon, the train **was** pulling out of the Vancouver train station and our long-awaited journey **had** finally begun.

We **had** been travelling on large boats for years, but travelling on a train **was** a completely new experience to my sister and me. Naturally, as kids, we **had** to explore every nook and cranny of the train. Most of our time **was** spent in the glass-domed observation car, watching day and night as the British Columbia landscape went passing by.

Eventually we approached the Rockies. Until then I **had** never seen anything so wondrous in my young life. It was absolutely stunning!

Now that I am in my early twenties, I often look back at the incredible trip and wonder if I will ever **have** such an overwhelming experience again. I'm sure that I will never **have** a vacation like that again.

Did you ever **have** a childhood experience like that?

5. Helping Verbs: Modal Verbs

1. He **could** have returned the library book yesterday without a fine; however, today he cannot do that.

2. I will **have** to buy more bulk paper if I want to print out a complete copy of the essay tomorrow.

3. I **must** inform you that your interesting short story "My Life as an Over-ripe Tomato" does not meet our publishing needs at the present time.

4. You **should** take a glove to the baseball game just in case a foul ball is hit in your direction.

Answers

5. Darcy should have **taken** a glove to last Friday's baseball game since a foul ball landed right in front of her.

6. Thomas **used** to worry about final exams; however, now he meditates and takes yoga and doesn't worry as much anymore.

7. The family **would** rather visit St. John's in the summer than during a severe winter blizzard.

8. The weather person on the television says chances are good that it **will** rain tomorrow.

9. Marcie **could** have been accepted into the prestigious computer science program if her mark in calculus had been one letter grade higher.

10. Correct.

11. Jeff **had** better listen to the coach's warning or he **will** be thrown off the varsity team.

12. I **may** have left my bank card in the ATM.

6. **Verbs Followed by Gerunds or Infinitives**

1. I would hate **to lose** the opportunity for the job.

2. He remembered **to place** his key on the night stand by the window. (NOTE: *placing* is also acceptable, though it conveys a different meaning.)

3. Jennifer was homesick for Kamloops and missed **taking** walks along the Thompson River.

4. Mr. Sanji quit **playing** squash after he tore some knee cartilage and needed surgery.

5. Our whole floor in the residence volunteered **to pack** groceries at the food bank.

6. Thankfully, my uncle persuaded me **to sell** all my high-technology stocks.

7. Everything has been tabulated, and now I would like **to announce** the winner of the frosh week worm-eating contest.

8. I would like Gretchen **to meet** with me about claiming her grand prize.

9. Be quiet and listen to the creek **babbling**.

10. Help the lady with two broken arms **open** the heavy door.

11. Due to illness, the award-winning author postponed **coming** to Saskatoon.

7. **More Practice with Verbs Followed by Gerunds and Infinitives**

George Chuvalo started <u>to box</u> at an early age. He decided <u>to turn</u> professional at the age of 19 and won the Canadian Heavyweight Championship in 1956. His victory was claimed <u>defeating</u> James J. Park. Many boxing fans remember Chuvalo <u>standing</u> toe-to-toe with the great

Muhammad Ali and <u>exchanging</u> brutal blows. Numerous boxing commentators acknowledge Chuvalo as <u>being</u> the greatest, or at least toughest, Canadian heavyweight boxer ever. He always knew his limitations and strengths and never pretended <u>to be</u> a finesse boxer. Rather, he challenged himself <u>to be</u> the best he could be with the skills he had. Chuvalo expected <u>to win</u> whenever he entered the ring, and that confidence always showed in his determined performances.

Since he quit boxing <u>to pursue</u> other areas of interest, Chuvalo has been a much sought-after speaker at Canadian high schools. Through his speeches, he helps students <u>avoid</u> the ravages of drug use.

8.   Phrasal Verbs

1. I threw out the dog food that Ace hadn't bothered to touch.

2. Correct.

3. Jack, Ali, and Jon met for a few hours to go over their group report before they presented it to the class.

4. After she had her operation, Nelson looked after his grandmother for a few days.

5. Correct.

6. The clerk in the administration offices handed me another form and told me to fill it out.

7. Because of inclement weather, race organizers decided to call off the race in benefit of the hospital and various children's charities.

8. Correct.

9. After the hot summer we had, many people will look into installing pools.

10. Once the party is over, a crew will clean up the mess.

9.   Using Appropriate Verb Tenses in Conditional Sentences

1. When a solar eclipse occurs, the moon **blocks** out the sun.

2. You **win** the jackpot if three aces appear on the slot machine.

3. Whenever Selma prepared her notorious undercooked chicken, her dinner guests all **got** sick.

4. If I don't get the position I want with IBM, I **will apply** to another corporation.

5. If they had a place in the country, they **would keep** horses.

6. If you try to play squash without properly warming up, you **will pull** a muscle.

7. You **will receive** a passing mark if you study the material we covered in class.

8. The children **will catch** colds if they go outside without their coats.

9. If I had ignored the financial advisors at my local bank, I **would have** more money in my portfolio today.

10. Editing for Appropriate Verb Tenses in Conditional Sentences

It seems that whenever humans invest in space exploration, the spin-offs in terms of scientific knowledge and technological development have been amazing. If scientists and planners are correct in their predictions, this will be true of the International Space Station. In fact, some medical researchers think we may develop new drugs for the treatment of, and possibly a cure for, cancer if medical research conducted in space-station laboratories proves as fruitful as expected.

Here is just one exciting medical area where space-station research could lead us. More pure protein crystals may be grown in space than on Earth. Analysis of these crystals helps scientists better understand the nature of proteins, enzymes, and viruses. If scientists better understand these fundamental building blocks of life, perhaps they will be able to develop new drugs. If this research progresses as scientists think it will, it will lead to the study of possible treatments for cancer, diabetes, emphysema, and immune system disorders.

Many people question the amount of money spent on space exploration and research., but if it is not, these exciting possibilities for medical advancement would be delayed or even lost. In fact, if we had only invested more money earlier, medical science would be further along today.

11.   Using Correct Verb Tenses with Indirect Quotations

6.   ANS: A

7.   ANS: B

8.   ANS: C

9.   ANS: B

10. ANS: B

12. Words You Can Omit and Those You Cannot

1. The British Columbia coast line **is** very irregular.

2. Round homes do not have the surface area of conventional homes; therefore, **they** lose less heat.

3. **There** are countless sound reasons for reducing greenhouse gas emissions.

4. As you will note from my comments at the end of your essay, **it** is clear that you must closely check your final essay copy for grammar and spelling errors.

5. **It** is a long way to Tipperary.

6. The biology teaching **assistant helped** me understand how osmosis contributes to kidney function.

7. The package Aunt Lil **sent contained** her inedible fruit cake as a Christmas gift.

8. Wanda often parks in the spot that I want to park **in.**

9. The college where she is **enrolled has** an award-winning design program.

10. The sports **car can** reach amazing speeds in mere seconds.

11. At the press conference, the Olympic athlete said **there** are many reasons for her early retirement from the sport.

12. Late at night, **it** can be quite dangerous to walk alone in that part of the city.

13. Placement of Adjectives and Adverbs

1. An oblong red Chinese box arrived only yesterday.

2. The modern Mexican gold bracelet dangled loosely from her wrist.

3. Correct.

4. Charles Lindbergh successfully crossed the seemingly endless grey Atlantic Ocean.

5. Then I looked for a narrow lime-green silk tie to go with my tapered blue corduroy shirt.

6. In the garage, Gavin tripped over the first tiny green garden gnome.

7. Stephen has occasionally managed to complete daring new backward dive.

8. Correct.

9. Jason is rather quiet around an imposing large older crowd.

10. The stuntwoman's fall was fortunately broken by the soft large rectangular mattress.

11. Gordon's Lightfoot's best early songs are frequently beautiful ballads.

12. Kati delicately placed the two German porcelain figurines on the table.

14. Present and Past Participles as Adjectives

1. Tim made a very <u>insulting</u> remark about Adul's weight, and I was most <u>insulted</u> by the tone he used to make the comment.

2. The novel *The Corrections* was a very <u>satisfying</u> read.

3. Wheat is surely one of the most important crops <u>produced</u> in Saskatchewan.

4. My eighty-five-year-old aunt had a <u>tiring</u> return flight to Vancouver.

5. After studying for three consecutive nights without any sleep, Quan had a very <u>tired</u> look on his face.

6. For Dustin, it was an <u>overwhelming</u> task to learn to speak a foreign language fluently.

7. The documentary offered a <u>fascinating</u> look at polar ice caps.

8. Most urban drivers display an <u>appalling</u> lack of courtesy towards fellow motorists.

9. The doctor is very <u>interested</u> in stem-cell research.

15. Correctly Using Prepositions to Show Time and Place

Part 1

a. We plan to hold the meeting **in** two weeks **in** the floor lounge.

b. I have been **in** Moose Jaw before, but not **at** this time of the year.

c. Correct.

d. Correct.

e. **At** night, it is difficult to read street numbers **on** the front of a house.

f. In the daytime, she found it difficult to sleep **on** a plane.

g. She aimed her last shot **at** the 8-ball.

Part 2

Your are cordially invited to the marriage of

Jillian Wendy Solnicki

and

Russel Wing Singh

on Saturday, June 7, 2004

at 11 o'clock **in** the morning

at St. Bart's Ukrainian Church

in the town of Alton, Ontario.

Reception will follow

in the Kon-Tiki Room

at the Alton Inn.

1.   Using Words Correctly

1. Despite his strong convictions, Jacquim is not **averse** to having a drink of good wine on

    special occasions.

2. After years of diligent practice, the swimmer is **all ready** for the Olympic trials.

3. The prime minister **alluded** to his chief rival when he mentioned the short-lived popularity of

    former Prime Minister Kim Campbell.

4. The choice of starting point guard for the junior varsity basketball team is **between** Stephanie

    and Clarissa.

5. It requires a certain set of **climatic** conditions for a hurricane to occur.

6. Sandra was extremely **discreet** for not divulging her roommate's numerous psychological

    problems.

7. The master of ceremonies gave a glowing introduction to the visiting professor that was

    highly appropriate for such an **eminent** guest.

8. The agent had trouble selling the house after prospective buyers found out there had been an

    illicit hydroponic garden in the basement.

9. Uncle Nick advised me to **proceed** with caution when exploring old mine shafts.

10. **It's** my favourite quote from T.S. Eliot's *The Wasteland*.

11. At the club, Margaret spent hours and hours riding the **stationary** bicycle.

12. If you are not sure of the name of the person who holds the position when you write the

    letter, address it "TO **WHOM** IT MAY CONCERN."

NOTES

NOTES